D0095293

headed *for the* blues

josef

skvorecky

headed
for the
♪ **blues**

a **memoir**

with **ten**

stories

Alfred A. **Knopf** Canada

PUBLISHED BY ALFRED A. KNOPF CANADA

Copyright © 1997 by Josef Skvorecky

All rights reserved under International and
Pan-American Copyright Conventions. Published in
1997 by Alfred A. Knopf Canada, Toronto. Distributed
by Random House of Canada Limited, Toronto.

Canadian Cataloguing in Publication Data

Škvorecký, Josef,
    Headed for the blues: a Memoir with ten stories

Includes bibliographical references.

ISBN 0-676-97043-5

1. Škvorecký, Josef, 1924–   – Biography.
2. Authors, Canadian (Czech) – 20th century – Biography.*
I. Title.

PS8537.K86Z53   1997   C891.8'6354   C97-930398-0
PR9199.3.S57Z47   1997

First Edition
Printed and bound in the United States of America

To my lifelong friends
P. L. Dorůžka and Ludvík Šváb

and to Dan Halpern,
who's always had trust in me

contents

headed

for the

blues

N EUILLY, a quarter, a street, a movie theater, a scene from a film, the August sun filtering through the leaves of the chestnut tree onto the beige lace curtain, pregnant women in prison (we're told), as soon as the baby is born, mother goes either to the gallows or to the separate solitude of a women's camp, but the infant, not destined for adoption like the children of Lidice,[1] is dispatched straight to its grave, tiny mounds of soil surrounded by the vigorous tunneling of blind moles, deserted little graveyards. I arrived home, in the passageway Přema showed me a pistol. "All you gotta do is stick it under somebody's nose," I flip back to my first, my oldest memory (they say everybody has one). Is everybody's about death? Mine: a run-over frog on the road that runs along the lovely Ledhuje River in the beautiful twenties, it must have been before I could talk, discern, know, all I could do was to take in, through the primary structure of my cerebral cortex, the lovely dusk by the Ledhuje, the rustling silver crowns of the young willows, as I knelt in my old-fashioned stroller with its carved backrest, propelled by the one who gave birth to me through the old, tranquil, peacetime town, no end to its beauty, and there, before me on the road lay the frog, its guts popping out of its burst belly, and Přema had a childhood dream of a paradise called Popovice, a world even lovelier (if that's possible) than Kostelec; in a fit of childish defiance, a naive childish act of rebellion he set out, he disappeared, some fellows from the railroad found him two kilometers past Kostelec, a scrawny little boy striding resolutely from tie to tie between the railroad tracks, because don't all roads lead to Popovice, with a child's mental associations, he knew that you take the train to get to Popovice, and the train goes on the railroad tracks, but when they found him, he hadn't made it to Paradise, and he told me about the transmitter: he'd stolen it when he was in the army in '45, he had barely finished hiding the machine gun his cousin Bob had stolen back in '38, he was always confident that the war wasn't going to end, not in our lifetime, and you never know when one thing or another will come in handy. And so he had the short-wave transmitter concealed in his wardrobe, but I wasn't that unequivocal any more, maybe I had never been that sure, that steadfast, I (simply) never knew anything for certain, and this was a few months after the president died, and Benno and I spent nights of our (waning) youth in long discursive conversations lying in the widow Ledvinová's bedroom and Benno spoke like Demosthenes, gnawing away at me, in me, the way he used to when there was still a Social Democratic Party, but I was never sure of anything, certainly not of any political party, it wasn't out of apathy, no, the exact opposite, and also out of fear, I was always beset by terrors, I couldn't help it, the Hell I'd heard about in catechism classes, the airborne gas war (gas marks in '38, before the mirror I was transformed into a monster from Mars and scared the hell out of myself), and before that, vampires in fairy tales told by our maid (in those days maids still existed), later she jumped under a train, I was alone, my parents downtown in a nightclub till late at night, the apartment full of ghosts and bats, vampires, murderers, I locked myself in the toilet, and stood in there, my back to the door, eyes popping out of my head, facing the window onto the air-shaft. And beyond it, shadows, and the midnight wind howling, my folks downtown at the bar, the howl of the saxophone, I'd wake up drenched with my own frozen sweat, then there were the concentration camps, Auntie Pavla in faraway Russia, Mr. Katz the teacher in nearby Auschwitz, early on in the war they sent back a little tin coffin with the remains of Lieutenant Peninger, inescapable terrors, anxieties which, like Přema, I knew would never end, never in the years of our lives, greater or lesser anxieties, the lesser ones always a portent of the greater ones, and so I didn't knuckle under. But gnawed away at by Benno, the fat trumpet player from the pharmacy, I fell victim (almost) to the seductive call of an explicitly defined paradise, the illusionism of ignorance, it truly seemed to me (and not just to me) that everything would be so simple, and it would bring about the birth of universal brotherhood; NO. I didn't like that word, I was never capable of intimacy; I believed in a facile socialism, a word which was then still untainted with any of its later connotations, I'd already fought with it before, with the specific uncertainty called Zoshchenko, Akhmatova, the Soviet Art Exhibition,[2] I knew (surely I must have known) that it would mean the end of freedom for me, who, for better or for worse, looked to words for meaning, content, happiness, or simply for life, words put together by the extravagant method of *belles lettres*, beautiful prose, but it wasn't clear to me whether this extravagance was *unum necessarium*, and whether there weren't more important things in the world than ME, and so whether I ought not to give up the privilege of the freedom of Extravagant Words, nothing was ever entirely clear to me, and that was when Přema said that his cousin Bob, a British subject, had been here and gone (bearer of the Victoria Cross) and that they had agreed upon a code, a wavelength. "We're going to be transmitting, I need you, because it has to be in English." I didn't want to, but Přema was my buddy from way back, can anyone understand, he was never an intellectual, didn't care for the band, didn't like students, the lone observer on the evening promenade, a shy, chaste adventurer, he took off the spring before the war, his plan: to swim the Morava River, to cross Slovakia on foot to Poland and the army, but he was barely fourteen, they slept over in a house under construction, near an open coke fire that gave off warmth and toxic gasses, the bricklayers found them half poisoned and herded them back home. So he used to cut telephone wires, refused to learn German, got expelled from business school, when he worked at the Lufthansa factory he poured sand into aircraft engines, but he survived to say to me, "Come on. I need you." I came. The transmitter in the wardrobe, I sought the prearranged signal among the murmur of the world, I transmitted the signal out into the babble of the world, silent beside me sat Přema and Vašek, the greengrocer who spent his days in his little delivery van, a hard working freckle-faced redhead, neither of them knew the language, and I was transmitting the signal, my mind on the three vehicles they always used for triangulating the location of transmitters, Kostelec as usual in the vice of fear, no luck, then home by night, torn with ambivalence between friendship and my uncertainty about right and wrong, the eternal question that I will never shake, not even over the new little Herodian graves, babies born in jail, mothers to the gallows, because maybe I'm stupid, I can't fully believe what my eyes haven't seen, but isn't there something even worse than the death of innocents, still unaware, their lives only a wavering mist, a sense of irritation, soon extinguished, soon they fell asleep, isn't what I know for certain worse yet, after all, they admitted it, they didn't deny it, right under the Communist daily's motto "Every morning, *Rudé Právo*," I saw HIS signature, A. Dubček, after all, so many executions that the Ministry asked them to slow down, the executioners are exhausted, an execution is hard on the nerves, comrades, and after all, I remember *clearly* reading what the sentences were, eighteen, nineteen-year-olds condemned to fifteen to twenty, after all a person is *not* responsible for his faith in this idealism or another, because at eighteen, *nobody* means anything but well, after all, no one is indifferent at eighteen, because at that age, no one is calculating, but they were arrested (the eighteen-year-olds) because they believed in an idealism different from that of those who arrested them, isn't that worse than stories of dead innocents among the moles, which may even be apocryphal; their waiting in the cell, just waiting, and mornings, the order "Shave!" and watching (related Ota) all three of them in the death cell lather up, darting glances at one another, because only one of them would be hanged, and afterwards, they couldn't help themselves, it was so obvious, the other two freshly shaved ones would sigh with relief, at least one more day of life ahead of them, the third freshly shaved one vanished down the hall to the courtyard, the terror, the horror of socialism, and hadn't I seen, in that Party document, over the signatures of B. Kolder, A. Dubček,[3] they forced them to eat their own feces, then why not believe in innocents down among the moles' pantries, it's no worse, it's only the sentimental cliché that evokes a greater disgust, but not the horror brought on by the terminal shaving scene. But it's done. What's done is done. People leave the cities for the cooperative farms, things are fine in the villages, nobody wants a return to private farming, they have modern apartments, cars, TVs, what if I was right after all? What if the sweet extravagance of words is important to me, but I am not important, what if Orwell was right, and they'd develop a race that didn't have that need, what if freedom is a premature extravagance, a luxury (as they claim it is)? Then those graves—no: they were not necessary, but to tear down the gradually strengthening organization of Utopia, on their account—I never knew anything. Back then I knew neither about the little graves nor about feces and it was an awful night for me, friendship versus uncertainty, what to do? and then came morning, and afternoon in the woods on the banks of the Ledhuje River, across from where Irena lived in the magical domain of waning youth, I met Přema's uncle: "What did that kid do, have you any idea?" Fright. They had come for him. He had escaped. Jumped out the window, just like that, in shirt and trousers.

Home, and sure enough, there he was, Přema, nervous but contained. I gave him a sweater, money, after dark he snuck outside and away through the woods to the next town, where he would take the express train to Prague. We had a plan. My uncle the Member of Parliament, he'd know something, he'd find somebody, it'd cost something—but my uncle didn't know anything, he was horrified, how could he have known anything, my uncle, he'd been stunned when it all began in '48,[4] "What's happening? What's wrong?" and the whole week, when the socialist realist militia were tramping through town and easily, handily slashing our world and its old certainties, he sat by the radio listening, he didn't go to the Parliament, he knew nothing. In the hall, my cousin would open letters: "The Action Committee has divested you.... The Action Committee has expelled you."[5] My cousin wailed, howled, a helpless howl, and that was when I knew that all was lost forever, that in fact there is a wheel, *jenseits von Gut und Böse*,[6] a dark and heavy wheel, that no one will ever be able to turn back, and from that moment on the bank of the lovely Ledhuje River, I knew that the world of loveliness is transitory, but a little corpse with its guts protruding from a burst belly is eternal. So I knew that when my cousin howled, it was forever. And I despaired, but I thought of what the Reverend Father Meloun, that comical saint, had instilled in me, the supranatural conviction that I have no right if my neighbor also has no right, even at that moment of despair I wasn't sure whether things were not in fact as they should be (Benno's gnawings), very few of them had villas like my uncle, why should one have a villa while another—I don't know. After all, by then there was no poverty. Not in our country. And no man is an island entire of itself,[7] if a clod be washed away by the sea, Europe is diminished, and with it, the world. No, I don't know a thing. Then came the time of exhausted executioners, now comes the time of hogs and TV sets, young workers getting paid more than old doctors. What, forget? Believe? My uncle didn't arrange anything but at another clandestine meeting in some apartment or other, maps, another plan: the next day was the president's funeral,[8] all the cops would be pulled into Prague. Trains were still running to Germany in those days: "There's a steep hill about two kilometers before the border and the train has to slow down, you'll jump off, go the rest of the way across the border on foot through the woods." He made it. He didn't get caught. Přema.

Neuilly twenty years later, Neuilly of despair, like the howl of my cousin (they got him too, he was drafted early in the age of exhausted executioners, some NCO was giving a political lecture on freedom of religion as approved by the government, my cousin [who was devout] couldn't resist speaking up and they arrested him for inciting the troops. And my uncle, that nice, probably terribly selfish, very devout old-world uncle said, "After all, I know Gottwald[9] from Parliament. Twenty years. He always said hello to me. I'll write him. For me, he'll do it." Poor old foolish uncle. After that, he still cast his vote for the Constitution[10] which would employ the executioners, and he didn't get nominated in the first election with no selection. But he was fortunate, he was an old man, he retired and for another five years, surrounded by old Jesuit periodicals, he worked on an anti-Marxist treatise: the last of his ludicrous acts, he would never understand that exploitation is an economic category and not the indignant words of a preacher, and he compiled a chronicle of his friends, small factory owners, fair-sized entrepreneurs, honest estate owners who never failed to pay a fair wage, and hence—but then he even stopped work on that and lived to a ripe old age. Luck was with my cousin, too, what happened to him was before the age of class awareness [the executioners weren't up and running yet], he only got six months, but it did mean goodbye to law school. So he lived the ordinary life of the proud sweet bourgeoisie: low-ranking foundry worker, rise at half past four, commute, home by seven at night, years of that, working his way up to shift boss, night school, by my time in Neuilly he was already a technical draftsman and his wife was dying of cancer. Ah, all those petty bourgeois, their wives, their princess daughters in their silk underwear, funny how reality never resembles socialist realism: When trees were being chopped down, how they [and their wives] worked on drill presses, in mines, with the black barons,[11] how—while the others stayed back in the mines, in the woods, at the drill presses—how persistently they rose again to penetrate the so-called structure of the new man, not for the love of profit, but because they were the bourgeoisie, the underpinnings of the world. Diligent, capable, creative, stubborn, opinionated, incorrigible. Dagmar, once in a mansion overlooking lovely Kostelec, today in a charming little inn in the Sierra Nevada in the fragrant woods of beautiful California, prettily plump, her hands rosy from washing dishes, the inn, a veritable *Work of Art* [dear Sinclair Lewis], while the mansion, erected from wartime profits, is now a training center for managers from the ranks of labor [before that it was a training center for the Ministry of Internal Security, and what was taught there? Torture? Didn't I read it with my own eyes under the motto "Every morning . . ." and below it, B. Kolder, A. Dubček]. How everything, how nothing fits.). But in Neuilly, outside the window the miracle that is Paris, my wife had gone to sleep already because it was all beyond her, she didn't realize, maybe she just refused to realize that her own city, the place she had spent her whole life, was gone forever, because she is my wife (but not for that reason alone). The city where she had felt hunger, real hunger, something that doesn't exist there any more, something never experienced by authors of socialist realist novels, something that still exists only in those novels, and then, in the age of the executioners—but she has written it far better,[12] why carry coals to a coal mine, that everyone knows. Anyway, she had gone to sleep, and I stayed up with Sylva and the wine in that luxury two-story flat in Neuilly, I felt a bitterness, she read aloud, short stories, she talked about the theater and her work there which she can't abandon, her face actually glowing in that beautiful Neuilly night, reciting stories, suddenly I recognized that I was the one it was all over for, not Sylva, not the Sylvas, because I am old, tangled up in the configuration of things over which I have no control, unlike her and the others her age. How old was she in the age of exhausted executioners? One. One year old. Back then I was reciting things too, equally avidly, to Lizetka[13] in Radlice, there was wine there too, and, like Sylva on her beloved stage, I scribbled away at desk-drawer writings— they overshadowed everything for me—we hid everything, the mechanism of the indifference of historical processes: the ones who were as old then as I was in Neuilly, they were the ones who were eradicated. Some on the gallows, others merely denied any hope of ever being published in the future, whereas I—well, I too had no hope, I never was a socialist realist, but I was twenty, and (to me) it seemed that even the future wasn't all that long. And perhaps all of that—theater, writing for desk drawers—is an extravagance, maybe they're right about that. But, because it is an extravagance, it's all the more likely to be the truth. That's a big word, I know, we never know all the truth. But all of it that we know, we must tell. Otherwise our extravagance is an affront to the ones who died, fled into exile, killed themselves, for their own extravagance—which even the Utopians say will someday be everyone's daily bread, come Utopia. So then isn't the extravagance of falsehood an affront to Utopia? It surely is, an even greater affront than the unwitting babble of the stubborn and ignorant, because that perhaps can resonate (at least can resonate) with common sense, while the extravagance of the falsehood of extravagant words resonates with the sound of a noose tightening. An executioner coughing. And: To every thing there *is* a season, a time to speak and a time to keep silence; a time to write novels and a time to write detective stories, Láďa,[14] that's not the whole truth, what do you know, the dilemma between the fragrance of your native soil and an American expressway, between the (officially sanctioned) adherence to the certainty of what they call your native soil and its prudent (fictitious) populace, and the (proscribed) responsibility of a contemporary intellectual to seek the truth (as much of

it as can be found) about the world of exhausted executioners, instead of the world of ideological festivities. But I
know. It isn't your fault (perhaps), and you've already said
enough in metaphors. But you might have shut up. Or written detective stories. I don't know if we have the right to say
only part of what we know, when my cousin is still alive,
when they, the ones who stalk souls oppressed by fear (fear
of the past that may very well become the present and ulti-
mately may have to become the future), the stalkers only
need for you to say something, just some small thing, something that doesn't even trouble you yet (otherwise why
would you be sending me a postcard on which you're afraid
to sign your full name?). But what do I know. Not as much
as they know about you, in their computerized files in the
tile tower.[15] I don't know.

In Neuilly, Sylva's eyes blazed with the safer flame of
those who will never set out on the terrible path of words
(which always leads to a bitter end), so they can travel safer
roads leading to a different, perhaps more bearable, bitterness; they blazed. I knew they would soon forget this *annus
mirabilis*, this summer of no Grace (or else I'm mistaken,
maybe I'm mistaken) and the pyrotechnical world of being
young would again exist in parallel with the world of exhausted executioners, which today is perhaps just the world
of exhausted investigators, the overworked *fizls*[16] that I
(perhaps) don't even see as cynics, perhaps they have truly
embraced the faith in the inequality of capable and incapable, in the right, in fact, the obligation (of the capable; but
capable of what?) to decide for others about others, because
the converse faith would writhe in the wild spasms of sweet

freedom, in the tumult of the world in which I now live, maybe they're right, we ought to forget. Or just not talk? But those who are able, who were endowed with the extravagance of words by God or by their body's or soul's biological makeup, they surely haven't got that right.

Maybe it is only a matter of being able to silence oneself, to stifle the uncertainty. Because—is it possible to live in uncertainty?

Yes, it is. Indeed, I think nothing is possible but uncertainty if one is capable of the extravagance of words. One must balance every certainty with alcohol or a tacit uncertainty. Anyone capable of the extravagance of words must tell everything he knows, or not tell anything at all, or else tell about Sherlock Holmes or the Sleeping Beauty. I can't imagine that a spoken certainty can exist without an unspoken uncertainty behind it. In fact, I think that if I put everything I know into words, that is, all my uncertainty, then the most uncertain thing about it would be the uncertainty as to whether what I left unsaid (because I didn't know it) doesn't represent a certainty—which I yearn for, doesn't everybody?

Sylva's eyes were aflame, and I, and we, our and my attempt to find Truth will be forgotten, because perhaps it is the young, the happy ones (since they're perpetually oblivious) who are entering an age when only the diligent *fizls* grow weary, when the executioner is idle, and then what there is is pure humor, not the black, André Breton kind, a more tolerable one. And somewhere, even more forgotten than I am, somewhere under leveled earth, under untended grass are the graves of tiny children who never knew the sweet milk of their mothers' breasts, which, untouched by infants' lips, lurched on the horrible swing of the age of exhausted executioners, the age of our youth, *when I swing by the string / I shall hear the bell ring*[17] (but that was the seventeenth century, not the century of the split atom). Perhaps brutality (they tell us) is necessary (Why? So there can be social benefits instead of welfare? Maybe that's the question when you get right down to it.); if it is necessary, then it can't get by without brutal people. But those who are capable of holding that horrible noose in their hand won't be moved by little graves, by tiny skeletons nibbled clean by little worms who in turn end up in the moles' winter pantries.

Then I wrote a letter to Australia, to a soldier I had once procured a chubby sleeping companion for, after five years of abstinence in a POW camp. I don't know if he ever got the letter, you had to take letters overseas to the post office in person and show your ID, they checked to make sure that the return address was the same, and I couldn't do that because the letter was asking him for help for a "defector." In fact, I'm sure he never got it. Besides, it was three years since that evening in the Prague apartment when Přema had stood across from me, his narrow, gangsterish face with the sad eyes as solemn as in a bad epic movie, I hated goodbyes, I simply shook his hand, said "Bye," and that was how we made our farewells (probably forever).

The next day a procession that marched on the fringe of history[18]: black robes with red chalices identified pastors of the Czechoslovak Church who were soon to be transformed into a mockery (some of them—others went to work as bricklayers, or as miners, or with penal military units); butchers in the costume of their guild, brazen and defiant; a

steely day, maybe it was raining, there were also members of
the Unitarian clergy, I stood on the embankment, emotional
women wept, of course, some women weep easily, but perhaps they could tell, with their woman's sixth sense that the
corpse, which was slowly passing through Prague, was the
final, by now only symbolic hand pushing against the chests
of the executioners, somewhat recovered by then from their
wartime and postwar harvest, reaped in a world where they
make life-and-death decisions with the stern justice of men[19]
dealing in death without being in any danger of it—how
easily, how easily—like my cousin's wail, there was yet another moment three years before, I was on my way from the
brewery where the half-killed bodies of SS-men (perhaps SS,
certainly men in uniforms, apparently German ones) were
still twitching, and Herbert Percy Siddell (his real name, he
may still be living in Manchester), his face a greenish hue,
said, "Don't you have a gun? Can't you get me a gun? Why
don't they finish them off?" *Coup de grace*, ah, but, only aris-
tocrats knew mercy, this world, born of the surrealist union
of cannibal and machine gun, knows no mercy. "How can
they let them lie here like this?" said Siddell the butcher (I'm
not being metaphorical here, he was in fact a slaughterhouse
worker) who five years earlier had been in the Old English
crowd on the beach at Dunkirk, he had stuck there and fired
and kept on firing until everyone was loaded up on boats
which vanished towards the shores of Albion, only then did
he surrender, according to old military codes dating back to
the times before the union of cannibal and armored vehicle.
I had no gun, but even if I had one, I wouldn't have been
able to finish them off, perhaps it was the Reverend Father

Meloun in me, my alter ego, who at his worst was capable of the marriage registry fraud that had saved the lives of a few Jewish girls in antedated mixed marriages. Anyway, I was on my way from that brewery, my spirit crumbling, gone all the joy (what there had been of it) over the war's ending— perhaps that was when my incapacity for certainty took root and as I walked past the Hotel Slavia, I saw Olda coming towards me, a fellow I went to grammar school with, he had a stutter, for me, a day of wrath, *dies irae, dies illa*,[20] an emaci- ated Jewish woman, fresh out of a concentration camp near Chudoba, got in an argument with the cashier at the Jasa delicatessen, it was over a chunk of salami, naturally she had no ration tickets and she was hungry, but the man at the counter, his whole war spent on complex dealings around ticket-free black market salami and in complex wheeling and dealing with butchers, with the shadow of concentra- tion camp hanging over his head (you could get sent to the camps for anything), inhibited by absurd fears (absurd in her mind, not in his) based on that old momentum, he refused to sell her the salami without a ration ticket, she screamed at him, he was embarrassed, everyone in the store was embar- rassed, when Mr. Bohadlo, the lawyer, opened his billfold (a word with no socialist realist associations) and with a mag- nanimous gesture (who knows what goes on inside a person? Was it phony? Did he really feel for her? Or both? And either way, would his deed, objectively, have been any less commendable?) gave the man at the counter all his meat ration tickets (of course, he had connections on the black market) and the man at the counter carefully weighed out a chunk of salami, not too big, and Mr. Bohadlo passed it to the Jewish woman, who immediately sank her teeth into it. After that the bodies of the still-twitching (possibly) SS-men, and now the stammering Olda, impudent and glowing with ingenuous joy, at first I assumed it to be the generic joy of freedom regained (as the *epiteton constans* described it), but I was mistaken. "I got m-m-m-married, m-m-m-man!" he breathed, as if he couldn't believe it himself (it was pretty unbelievable), it struck me as absurd in those days of shooting and broad patriotic feelings, which never quite reached me; absently, I asked, "Who's the lucky girl?" "You d-d-d-don't kn-n-n-ow her, she's from E-e-es-tonia," stuttered the impertinently joyful Olda. "An en-en-engineer!" That was even more incredible, Olda being a textile laborer, a proletarian, he never got past the fifth grade, he had five brothers, sort of a relay team, at one time or another during my years at school, I had each of them in my class: I'd always get promoted with one, another would always get left back, then the one that got promoted got left back and another got promoted while another got left back, Olda and I got promoted together from third to fourth grade, I think, and when I was promoted to fifth grade, there was Lojza. A family with a lower-than-average IQ, and to top it off, Olda had that stutter. And now, marrying an engineer!

I didn't understand until later, when stagehands from Prague started marrying female doctors from Leningrad. Estonian, that explained it. She had endured the age of exhausted executioners some ten years before we did, and then, caught between two noisy furies, first with a sense of hope and later with a sense of hopelessness, but always with the nightmare of the swiftly depopulated, massacred

and deported Estonian university behind her, she fled before
an army which was lauded in ballads by poets laureate and
editorials by fellow-travelers as the bearers of a splendid and
joyful etcetera, followed by the diligent, exhausted but in-
defatigable executioners (including in their ranks weary but
brave little soldiers, amateurs, who dashed in front of the
red-hot barrels of professional Prussian machine guns . . .
*("The battlefront road is long, it can't scare away our song, No
thought of death . . ."),*[21] the terrified lady engineer from the
depopulated, massacred university fled before this brave
army, its first tanks caught up with her in Kostelec, she happened onto a stuttering Olda, dear old working man, she
latched onto him, and some public official, overwhelmed by
the excitement of revolutionary days (read: the final days of
the war) married them, it gave her (perhaps) Czechoslovak
citizenship, but no matter what, that ecstatic stammering innocent hid her in his little working-class home in the Hadrnice district, among his five brothers and seven sisters
(brother Lojza dying of tuberculosis, but he didn't die),
there she somehow survived the brief hospitality that the
land extended not only to the army but also the exhausted
executioners (they worked effectively, systematically, deftly,
I know that for certain, not from having heard it second or
third hand, like the awful story of the little graves. By May
12th, they had picked up Professor Okulin, a Russian, and
he disappeared. He did not come back until eight years later,
when Khrushchev—confused, but deep in his crusty appa-
ratchik heart, probably a decent fellow—partly dissolved the
Gulag Archipelago. In 1930, the professor had given a single
night's refuge to an emissary from Paris to the Cossacks in

the Ukraine; they had caught the emissary and beat him until he divulged his itinerary, which included, for a single night, the name of Professor Okulin), yes, she survived it, and in a brief two years achieved her own little *Wirtschaftswunder.*

I was back in Kostelec when I ran into stammering Olda again, but he had changed, he was standing on the corner of the square in a double-breasted business suit and he was a manufacturer. True, a small manufacturer, but he asked me to join him for a glass of wine, we sat in the cool tart-smelling winery on the square, Přema's father joined us at the table (he was a legionnaire[22] who had lost an arm) and so did two or three other buddies from the west side of town, Olda picked up the tab for everyone, now he had one of those manufacturer's billfolds too (it still lacked any socialist realist associations) full of hundred-crown notes, or back then they might even have been thousand-crown notes, and we guzzled wine, evidently pretty rank wine, I wasn't much of a connoisseur in those days, and Olda, his necktie tacked with a genuine gold tie tack, told me about his company, a small tablecloth factory, his Estonian engineer wife had drummed up a loan and some machinery, they even had an exhibit at the Trade Fair, then came February,[23] but Olda kept right on manufacturing, he was one of the last to be liquidated, that is, his factory, not him, his class origin protected him. But no sooner had they put him and his wife out of business than she rounded up some stalls and some angora rabbits, and within the year they were back again liquidating the dynamic drive and initiative shown by the daughter of the 1940 Estonian nightmare and her three-year journey westward through scorched cities and devastated countryside, it is a memory, like a memorial to Renatka, daughter of a fittings manufacturer, first a cotton mill laborer, then a night school student, then a night nurse (the abiding history of my cousin), the mother of five, wife of a prisoner-cum-miner,[24] who then became an ordinary miner, then a refrigerator repairman, then an accountant in the repair shop co-op, ah, you golden youth, you children of the sweet bourgeoisie, you eternal and earth-bound developers of all the successful economies of the world. And today? Olda is back as a textile factory worker, the Estonian engineer works on a fully automated loom. Renatka back as a night nurse.

A procession of Falcons, Eagles[25] and students moved past the weeping women, it flowed like a dying river between cops, the day was steely. Přema jumped off the train, crawled through the bushes, reached the safety of the *Flüchtlingslager*. I think there was the small archbishop walking behind the coffin, a martyr, but who remembers him? Certainly not Sylva, Sylva in Neuilly eagerly reciting short-short stories written by her boss in the theater, the theater and the boss who was the reason for her returning, and the second Dark Age of the Czech Lands is even darker, but without exhausted executioners, just with the ranks of brown-nosers, informers and *fizls* substantially augmented, and so the Sylvas, like the guys in the big rock 'n roll bands, coast through the years like we coasted, life is sweet and stimulating, and even freedom, albeit murdered, is perhaps a little less dead than it used to be, maybe I'm mistaken, after all, the extravagance of words had never before been so thoroughly restrained, and yet still it surfaced, here and there, libraries (personal ones) are full of the vestiges of the sixties, and now and then they echo from the stages of little theaters, wild music sounds loud and clear, more than a match for them, and the country is blooming, or maybe just bloating, literature died but girls are alive, in miniskirts from uncles in the West, who thinks of the archbishop. Maybe I'm mistaken. Maybe a few of the hardliners (idealists? I hear they're sneered at), the ones the unemployed executioners slap around, the ones they leave to die of untreated kidney problems, who thinks of them? Unless the thought is the awful, "Their turn has come! Why feel for them? Did they feel for anyone in the age of exhausted executioners? They only speak out when their turn has come." But how has it come to them? After all, it's easy to endure this age, the age of *fizls* (corruptible ones at that). All you have to do is *Maul halten und weiter, weiter dienen,*[26] all you have to do is live in seclusion and say only part of what you know. What's that? Stubbornness? A bloated ego? Inertia? Idealism? Some sort of certainty? Power out of control? Premature prophets, penitent zealots.

After all, who is freedom actually for? Really for everyone? Or only for the few, mostly those hooked on the extravagance of words. And not even all of those: there are whole genres that can survive without it. For centuries they built splendid cathedrals without it. Is there truly such a difference between wanting to stay somewhere and having to leave to go looking for a job, or having to leave because you've been ordered to go with a job placement chit?[27]

But I'm forgetting. I'm forgetting the black gloom that just such a chit brought me, almost as bad as a prison sentence. I'm forgetting sweet like Evinka, the princess whose red fingernails got her tossed out of medical school, she got back in, although not a proletarian, she knew her way around, her charms were many and delightful and the young men in the blue shirts[28]—masters over destinies, masters over lives, masters (except not quite) over the future—enjoyed copulating, she copulated her way back into med school, but she drew the line at copulating her way to a placement chit for Prague. Ah, the magnificent bourgeoisie! She wanted terribly to be a doctor, she was prepared to employ ancient and shameful methods that are the byproduct of all dictatorships. But once a doctor, and even though she loved Prague (where she was born, where she'd lived her whole life in the intimate tranquility of a genteel flat on Letná Hill where the elevator opened right onto their private foyer), even though she loved her parents, obediently but genuinely (Mamá and Papá, she actually put the accent on the last syllable, like something out of a socialist realist satire of the bourgeoisie), even though she loved silk stockings and designer dresses from Mme Podolská[29] and a pleasant stroll in a brand-new hat (she even used to have her own milliner, there's nothing like that any more), in spite of all that, she refused to re-employ the method known to all tyrannies so she wound up placed in a job in Dukla way out in Eastern Slovakia. In a village with no electric light, in a single room with an outhouse for a toilet, but she was a skier, trained at the ski lodges of Štrbské Pleso, she'd toss her leather satchel over her shoulder and ski off to help a gypsy woman in labor. And that's not The Story of a Village Doctor, or The Medal and the Functionary. It's the tale of a young girl who took only one thing seriously: the Hippocratic oath. She married there, not a local boy, of course, he came from Prague too, his family used to be in furs. After fifteen years, they finally got to go back, she to Prague, but he to Ústí nad Labem. It's still that way, they live for the weekends, Fridays he comes in from Ústí by express train, a day or two in the intimate tranquility of the apartment (Papá dead, Mamá still alive) enjoying his time with the three dark-eyed girls, Monday mornings back on the train back to Ústí, five nights in the doctors' dorm; the life of the real builders of socialism, whose lives—as my wife says—the comrades were willing to sacrifice to the revolution. How easy to be willing.

And Lojza? A simple proletarian, got as far as grade four, in primary school. He always wound up getting it in the neck, he didn't know how to defend himself, a baker's apprentice, it never occurred to him to lie his way out of trouble or that laws are there to be circumvented. And so he ended up getting sent to the Reich, to Germany, where night after night and days too, he would bake bread out of bran, in Berlin, in Hamburg, in the air raid zones (who remembers? Who knows about the heroism of the airmen and the *Luftschutz*, the forced laborers ordered to go out as air raid wardens and be targets?), Lojza caught TB there. He returned a few days after his brother and the Estonian engineer got married; back then I thought that medicine was the only profession in the world that still made any sense, I was working in the hospital, they put Lojza under an X-ray, chief of medicine Dr. Sumtych pointed out the classical examples of the distinctive spots on his lung X-ray. Lojza grinned, clearly flattered by the attention of the white coats, and then, on our way home from the hospital, he boasted about his quickly forgotten adventures in the air raids. Dr. Sumtych gave him six months, administered a pneumothorax, so at least he could say he had done something. But life is truly full of amazing things. From the Reich, Lojza started writing me letters. I've always had this ability to make friends with people who were not from the world of my intellect, and I was fond of them.

> Dear Friend,
>   First off let me send you all my best. How are you? I am fine, I got a raise, I am pretty good in German already. I have lots of food, except not meat, but all the bread I can eat.

Life is an incredible joke. The family from the house in Hadrnice included not only the female Estonian engineer, but also an aunt who had married a small farmer in Slovakia, and had a daughter. It so happened the daughter got in trouble, what with the army lauded in laureates' songs and fellow-travelers' editorials. One of the oldest tales in the book, and they said it mightn't even have been a Russian, and besides, there may have been several of them. In those days, it was still a terrible disgrace in village life, shameful. But somebody had an idea, maybe it was the aunt. The mother-to-be wasn't showing yet, nobody knew about the bun she had in the oven, cousin Lojza in Kostelec had half a year to live, better an orphan than a bastard. So they sent Lojza to Slovakia, to a gala village wedding, the groom couldn't have cared less. Except for the fact that the festivities included a wedding feast, and after years of nothing but bran bread, Lojza finally filled his stomach. Six months passed, the little orphan was born and Lojza was still among the living. Twenty years passed.

Dear Friend,

First off let me send you all my best. How are you? I am fine. I have been appointed the chronicler of our Unified Agricultural Cooperative in Bzinec and I write various articles for more than five papers, sometimes even to ones with statewide distribution. Fact is they've never sent me back a single piece yet and I've got paid for every one. I'm growing a garden and I'm keeping a hog.

Years passsed, strange years of evil and good, probably not unlike all other years everywhere else, except more intense in everything. I tried to be unselfish, not from any innate tendency but rather as a matter of will, a legacy from that comical cleric, but no longer supported by the concept of Hell, in which I had long since quit believing.

Dear Friend,

First off let me send you all my best from the German Democratic Republic where we have traveled with a bus tour organized by our own Unified Agricultural Cooperative.

The letters kept coming with the regularity of compulsive twinges of conscience; maybe God was trying to tell me, every time I started to gain a sense of certainty, that nothing is certain. Back when they arrested Sašenka,[30] another bourgeois princess not even eighteen years old, and sentenced her to five years, I almost got involved and I said

to myself, five years! And what for? For nothing, or for
almost nothing.

> *Dear Friend,*
>   *First off let me . . . on a culture tour to see the Bratislava*
> *Opera . . . the hog is 300 kilograms, come Christmas we*
> *slaughter him,*

then all that garbage when I was attacked from all sides,[31]
me, with nothing but the most innocent of intentions. Lojza
knew how to stick up for me, though, he wasn't Orwell's
New Man, not quite. He kept sending news from bus tours
in Bulgaria, reports on the weight of his hogs. By then I was
living across the ocean already, and one of those who also
write but don't perceive words as an extravagance, don't
weigh their words but go ahead and lie because what is good
for the Party, as Lenin said, and it seems that lies are often
good for the Party, at least that's what they believe—if one
can believe that they believe—anyway, one of those types
calculated in a newspaper article how much money I had
made on my novel, the novel that I had poured my own
blood into,[32] the one I'd written in a period of crisis, just
one of my normal periods, I struggled with the text like an
old man with death, while other novels were being published and critics from the age of disconcerted *fizls* sang ac-
colades, naturally they were (probably) right and heaven
knows it wasn't glory I was after, it never was, there was a
time I may have wanted to use glory to impress girls, sheer
Freud, of course those who don't possess the extravagance
of words will never believe that it's a matter of life and not

money, of meaning and not your picture in the paper or your name in the credits, it's a matter of life, and truth (I know very well that's a word so mauled and manhandled that it's been smoothed down to a repulsive egg-shape, but there is no other word to replace it), a matter of life, I grappled with that novel, because nobody holds art in his hand, they banned it during that brief period when Sorry Tony[33] got up the gumption to launch a counterattack against the brief liberalization, poet Ivan Skála (they say of him, "Remarkably, he's good." But a good poet is one who is read, and there are very few of those. Seifert. Eliot. *"Because I do not hope to turn again / Because I do not hope"*)[34] gazed at me with a fishy smile. "It can't be published," he stated, "but instead, we'll publish . . . a second edition . . . of those detective stories of yours." Not that I hadn't put the same effort into them, not for the glory, not for the money. In them, it's a matter of life, too. But I didn't know: Is it a bribe? Or an indication that he respects my work, and because it can't, on account of the censors . . . Did the poet think like I do? Did he know it wasn't a matter of the money? After what was euphemistically called "the arrival of the armies,"[35] he protested but only briefly. Now he's composing verses again (good ones, they say) about social injustices committed abroad. Moreover, I didn't know if it wasn't Adlerian, the way it used to be Freudian: Could I be writing deliberately in such a way that they won't publish it? After all, I can tell as well as the next guy who knows his way around. That way I can say to myself: It was good, but, they wouldn't publish it because of the content. That way neither I nor anyone else could ever tell if it is truly any good. Am I so weak that the only strength in my texts is in their so-called guts? Maybe it wouldn't have taken much, I can tell, maybe a few sentences in two or three chapters. Do a few chapters a little differently. Are those sentences, the way I'd done them, so critically essential? Wouldn't it be harder to write about things that aren't on their Index,[36] about ordinary things, about safe parts of the past? I tortured myself, an odd suggestion, could I be colluding with the censors, maybe I am deliberately playing to their smash, an Adlerian illness that would allow me to avoid taking a dreaded exam, strange psychosomatics, so I tortured myself, but then came the *annus mirabilis*, and a little later, the book was published after all, and then what happened was like something out of a novel itself: not the fact that the whole edition of tens of thousands of copies sold out in a day, that was normal in those days, what I mean is the letter from the blind girl, like something out of Victorian fiction, somebody decided to put the novel into Braille, and she read my story of the beautiful Leona, and as they say in the jargon of alienation, she identified with that radiant daughter of Israel in her perpetual darkness, she grasped the eternal Christian message about conjugal love—like in a Victorian novel, the handwriting in the letter was blurred, maybe from tears (she had dictated it to her mother, so maybe they were the mother's tears) so maybe I am good for something after all (I'm such a silly Marxist, I think in those categories), at least I provided a blind girl from Smíchov a few dreams. For a blind girl, like a figure from a sermon. The way it happens so often, a moment when the finger of God reaches into the commonplace. A sentimental satisfaction. And in his article, the Writer-of-Lies-for-the-Good-of-the-Party calculated my income from the novel about the beautiful Leona as if he were writing about embezzlement, the possibility of something like the blind girl never entered his mind (just about the same time, another guy, worse because he was intelligent, tried to do Leona in with a kind of earnest sophistry: describing it as a trap for the reader, I ostensibly lure the reader, cleverly, almost perfectly, into my own vision of the world, of course I only view part of society [but I tell everything I see]. Once again, like something from one of my own novels inhabited by lovely girls, my symbol for a world in which beauty is always fleeting, once again who came to my defense but a girl from Karlovy Vary, she wrote a letter to the editor of *Tvorba*, the charming missive of an intelligent person, not intelligent with the conformist intelligence of the critic who wrote the review, but with the intelligence of all those Czech women readers of all the gloomy ages of our homeland—then they were still printing Letters to the Editor like this one, soon afterwards they quit). And from Lojza to Canada already,

Dear Friend,

First off, let me . . . I enclose an article by a certain Mr. Raneček . . . It seems to me that this comrade simply envies you your success. If he knew how to make money, he would make some too. They just published my 100th article which I also enclose. In the last 15 years, I have made about 5000 Crowns for my writings. It is not as much as you, my friend. But who would have thought back in Kostelec that both you and me would be authors? Well, and how are you in distant

Canada? This year, as every year, I have a hog, by Christmas he will reach 400 to 450 kilograms

—that too is a part of home, writers of lies for the good of the Party, intelligent lackeys (once in the age of disconcerted *fizls*, a lackey slipped up, or his cup of accumulated rage at having to bend his intelligence for the good of the Party overflowed, and he wrote a paean on a collection of poems that a friend of mine wrote, it's bass line was *"and arresting them all."*[37] After the entry of the troops, he returned to his senses.). "The Unified Agricultural Cooperative at Bzinec has celebrated its harvest festival," wrote my friend Lojza in his one-hundredth literary effort. "This year, as in years past, members of the Unified Agricultural Cooperative gathered," and so on and so forth. But not a single word of a lie, not a one. Not even a minor tribute to the gods from a hog-breeder, from the father of a daughter of at least three fathers. That too is the truth, back where we no longer live. Ota said, "So after their son was rehabilitated,[38] they asked for an exhumation so they could rebury him, but they were told that exhumation was impossible due to advanced decomposition and to the fact that the hanged man Sirový was eighth down in vertical order in the common grave." Grass grows from those bodies, in that grass grows clover, they will scythe it down, feed it to hogs, and then they will slaughter them.

They marched in the funeral procession, embittered, truculent, dragging with them the burden of a history as described by almost all the great writers of the age before the arrival of the executioners. They were ruled by money, virtues were tied in with the family, every man for himself, hypocrites, nationalists, capable of anything, maybe even killing, certainly capable of firing people, letting them go hungry, anything to maintain their business—but also amazingly tolerant (that is also obvious in the land of their ultimate refuge, I think for that very reason it's their land of hope); thousands of writers have described their black souls, their earthbound, petty, tiny little sordid souls, and all those doomsday judgments against the petty bourgeoisie, the system of merchants and entrepreneurs (peddlers and exploiters) have become part of literature, as so-called "triumphs of the human spirit and art"; it proved that the fundamental flaw was stereotyping: if they were embittered and truculent, a living monument to evil, they are at the same time a monument to an odd kind of good; a symbiosis of good with evil. And their particular good, called freedom (after all, weren't they the ones who gave birth to it, didn't they use it to demolish feudalism and the principles of servitude, *citoyens*, the bourgeoisie, the merchants and the financiers?) grew and continues to flourish. Nowhere was ever anyone as free as a citizen of the land that was their ultimate refuge. True, today as in the days of Stephen Crane, drunken wretches lie in the gutter in the Bowery, loathsome wrecks of humanity without a future. But those who leave the Bowery bums to their destiny have created a system in which one can steal the secrets of an army and sell them and become the hero of the day, one can deliver weapons to murderers and become the day's heroine. Those, then, are the dimensions within which the bourgeois soul operates. In our corner of the world, it was all about helping the Bowery, but don't lay a finger on the court that freed Angela,[39] and all that at the same time as stratified common graves; true, that's the past. But a five-year sentence for distributing excerpts from the Constitution (Ah, the pamphlets in the bourgeois lands! Their underground magazines, their Nixon-head chamber pots!), the death of contemporary literature, elderly mothers of emigrés to the West facing the local Party wheel: "Take care, Comrade! It's up to me, and if I say yes, you travel West—and if I say no, you stay at home!" Jackass, maybe he truly believes that he is the personification of sweet socialism. The death of literature. Bribes. Making hypocrites of everyone. The death of novels. Petty little souls, petty *fizl* souls. The death of plays, the death of the Eliots. Indolent, uninspired, obedient, since they knew one thing for certain: that their sweet socialism hinged on their obedience. The death of literature. The benefits are entirely material. Better (slightly better) health insurance (ostensibly); better (slightly better) old age security; paid maternity leave (of course, in the system of merchants, a man can support a woman). A few (fairly moot) points like that—but compared to the nonmaterial benefits of bourgeois life? Those wonderful books? The life of literature? The trials? The prisons and TVs smack in the public eye? The freedom to stay or leave, to speak or not speak, to drink yourself to death on the Bowery and to write *An American Tragedy*? What equivalent benefits does our land in the age of petty *fizls* have to offer?

Demagoguery. No, I am aware of the diligent, grubby apparatchiks, slaving away for the betterment of the system, first the executioners' system, now the *fizls'* system, who never

knew anything else, who truly believe that this here is better
(and isn't it? Workers in laid-back factories, sinecures, dis-
pensaries, subsidized plant cafeterias—compare them with
Chicago steel-plants, where the only thing better is the pay,
or perhaps some other things, if you're sneaky, if you know
how to rip off an insurance company; but if you're an ordinary factory worker, the only thing better is probably the
pay) and who try to sop up the pools of blood with tiny rags
of charitable acts; they try to outwait the death of literature in
suspended animation, waiting for Godot (Utopia) to arrive,
those small, simple-minded, grubby apparatchiks, those petty
district functionaries, those puny charitable clerics of the ages
of darkness and the Inquisition who sought to save (who
saved?) the reputation of the Holy Church; how absurd: the
typical socialist hero, the functionary who actually disobeys
the call to vigilance and refuses to abandon his unequivocal
faith in the integrity of one officially labeled Enemy of the
Working Class; the most individualistic of heroes, asserting
his own tiny individual truth against the error of the Party's
Great Truth? Isn't it absurd, and isn't it the only thing that is
truthful (albeit atypical and albeit far from ending happily) in
socialist realism? Anyway, I am aware of them. But they are,
after all, nothing but the petty clerics of the age of the Holy
Inquisition. Once upon a time they got together, they re-
belled, led by one of their number, a petty cleric named
Saša.[40] Sašenka. Well, and the tanks disbanded them. Not all
of them. Certainly, many remained, they are certainly trying. But what kind of a system is it that sublimates the good
in the character of the Great Individualist: the Functionary
with the Human Heart replacing the Party Heart?

And perhaps they are right. Isn't this world often a world of paradox, of the absurd? Perhaps the road to the Utopia of Freedom (as exists in the here and now in America) coupled with worry-free financial security (as used to exist in convents and continues to exist in peacetime armies and in classy prisons in the last refuge of the merchants) and peopled by great souls with no selfishness, no hypocrisy, no pettiness (the kind of souls who may be among us right now, here and there, and always have), perhaps that road leads across those graves (they shouldn't have happened, but they did; we won't desert the road on account of them); perhaps that road is flanked by rank upon rank of those *fizls*, staked out with edicts, bans and directives, perhaps its sentinel is a monstrously hypertrophic Lenin: what benefits the Party is moral (so, Arabs and Jews, murder your young men: what benefits the U.S.S.R. . . . history's greatest criminal is the Jew Kissinger); perhaps Utopia is made possible by the death (suspended animation) of literature (at least contemporary literature, literature critical of the social and the human status quo—radically critical. It seems to me that the literature that has survived, that genuinely—perhaps—affected something, not only in literature but even [perhaps] in society, was never anything else. I must be mistaken. After all, wasn't Shakespeare a toady to the establishment? Yes, he was. But he still went magnificently to the roots of life, in spite of the fact that he extolled the status quo in England with sycophantic verse. His age—the beginning of the age of merchants—allowed him to. Modern dictatorships enjoining those who cultivate the extravagance of words to come on side certainly don't allow them to go magnificently to the roots of life. Or so it seems to me. Wary, circumspect *fizls* even sniff around in the texts of historical dramas and mystery novels. Everything could be an allegory); such perhaps is the road to Utopia—why not? The essence of the world is, perhaps, Paradox (*credo quia turpe, amo quia absurdum*). Right? Is it possible to love the Great Petty Functionary, that tin god of the Party apparatus, the way Tertullian loved the sweet, superstitious, occasionally wrathful Christ, who nevertheless said, "Whosoever of you is without guilt," tin god of the selfsame Party that is and always was the most zealous caster of stones? It couldn't even confess without casting stones. Like the Holy Church. Can anyone? Any institution?

But if this is the road to Utopia, then Utopia will understand (it has to; otherwise it wouldn't be Utopia) that I couldn't have done any differently.

And I still can't. I try to serve the memory of Utopia. Let others pave the way. I still think that if it weren't for the ones who try to build bends into that inhumanly straight road, or even to barricade it, straight as it is, it would never get where it's going. It seems to me that the truth is with the dialectic (all that talk about *antago* and *non-antago*,[41] the good and the even better, indicate the decadence of the dialectic, a decline to sophistry, as at the dawn of our civilization—the tortoise quicker than the hare—from the greatness of Heraclitus' dispute about fire and water to the pettiness of the dispute about angels dancing on the head of a pin).

Back to the story? I should, shouldn't I. But I probably don't possess the gift of telling all I know, all my uncertainty, with only a story, the way they teach it in writing courses, the way Balzac did and Dickens, Tolstoy, Dostoyevsky. (Did they? With only a story? All they knew?) Perhaps we know too much already, more than they knew, too much to translate into a story (or: I don't possess that gift). I tried (*The Miracle*) and that was, perhaps (virtually. Virtually?), the entire repertoire of my capacities: people from the inside (me and others like me) and people from the outside (everyone not-me), rounded characters (Liška) and flat ones (Bukavec. Bukavec?), from real life (Ponykl) and from literature (Mr. Kohn. Mr. Kohn?); if you will: positive (Ivana Hrozná) and if you will: negative (the murderer Bárta; no, there is no way I can empathize with him); characters I love and, lacking bathos, I am unable to love any other way than through their ludicrous sides—it seems to me that is where their human face is (the wino poet, Father Doufal, Sweet Suzi, the lovely Sylva); characters whose destiny makes me cry; and: if you see me smiling, I'm smiling to keep from crying (Kopula, Mr. Pohorský); characters I admire for what they are (Sister Udelína); characters I admire for what they know (Dr. Gellen); characters I respect, for they did not create the world of exhausted executioners (Očenáš); characters I respect because they are trying to fix it (Vrchcoláb); characters I am fond of because they didn't change (Kocour, Fikar). A repertoire of procedures: logic, anecdote; the deliberate braiding of strands of plot to set up the point (the bride with the sliced-off nose-tip; the vicissitudes of Mr. Kohn and Sylva and Danny, meeting in the woods at the border; the running gag, that tribute to the old masters of clever two-reelers), which here they call skillful plotting; satire, contrast, a jeremiad into which I translate Terence's *Homo sum, nihil humani* . . . (the Mass in the Vincentinum, a chronic

care institution in the mountains, under Dr. Řeřicha's bon-
boniere sky); the *bon mot*, the wisecrack (I love wisecracks:
*the doomsday machine of the revolution . . . and on it they danced
Serbian circle dances and the dances of other folk*)[42]; and yes,
you're right, it isn't cynicism; one thing I know for sure:
cynicism is never in words, it is exclusively and always (call
it redundant; the art of words is grounded in redundancy
and not in grammar) in the deeds. But the startling and (to
me) incredible thing is how for some people, twenty ostensibly dirty words can obscure four hundred pages of a declaration of love for Life. How a reverend father (not Father
Meloun or Father Doufal or even that priest who compared
The Cowards to an admission in a confessional) can fill a
dozen columns trying to prove that Danny's relationship to
Irena is strictly materialistic, carnal, (isn't he always thinking
about her breasts, her thighs, etc., and, at best, of her lips and
her eyes?) and hence unworthy of man and Christian, and
manages to overlook the key scene (I love key scenes; key
sentences; the entire meaning of my messages—not all that
remarkable, in fact pretty ordinary, but certainly human, I
hope—is concealed in those easily overlooked sentences,
sentences easily overlooked by professional orators from far
right to far left: there is a sentence—or several—like that in
The Lion Cub, about socialism, and another about love—and
also in *The Tank Corps*,[43] one about socialism—and in *The
Emöke Legend*, about what enables us to live, which Graham
Greene didn't fail to register,[44] even in *The Bass Saxophone*,
about the essence of art—and so forth), the key sentence,
then, about Irena, about love: *"I thought frantically about her
body and I could feel how fantastically hot and alive it was and I*

loved it, but suddenly it wasn't only because of the pleasure it gave, because she'd denied that to me, but for the life in it, for the fact that it was Irena and because of that little soul of hers which was dumb, maybe, but was still the living and tortured soul of a woman."[45] I tried. I put everything into it that I had (everything? A person is always a little lazy. Or better said, a person tosses in the towel. I think it's generally a bit like that. You're working on some text, you dream about it at night. Your feelings oscillate between "a pile of shit" and "maybe it's passable." There are even passages that still seem beautiful to you, and when you go back and read them, you say, as John Wain did, *"I wrote this? Impossible. I cannot do a thing like that. It must have been someone else."* But as a rule, those are only brief passages, wisecracks, scanty formulations. Never—well, hardly ever—a whole book. And then you get to a point when you just toss it in. For better or for worse. Here I stand, God be merciful unto me, it's all I can do. And you send it to the printer.). So *perhaps* everything I had got I put into it. I tried. If I live, I shall continue to try. I'm not complaining, but it wasn't all beer and skittles. Nor for that matter was it entirely lacking in some (relatively brief) moments of joy.

But better to get back to the story, then: about Přema. They never found the transmitter. The age of executioners had not arrived yet: the arresting officers inherited by the age of incipient executioners from the age of the Dr. Mejzlíks[46] (and would soon be removed). They arrived at the flat and proceeded to pound theatrically (very hard) on the door (these didn't come at night, either), shouting raucously (I am serious, the words are authentic, I got it firsthand from the one-armed legionnaire Mr. Skočdopole):

"Open in the name of the law! We have come to arrest Přemysl Skočdopole." They kept on pounding until Přema jumped out the window and his one-armed legionnaire father let them in. Přema took with him, in a momentary lapse of lucidity, some pamphlets with a rather moronic appeal to the nation (the Kostelec Manifesto; these days they call them manifestos) that I had written on his request, and left the transmitter in the room. In front of the house, he ran into Benda, who wasn't even part of the conspiracy, just a buddy, and shoved the pamphlets into his hands: "Burn these!" and proceeded to our house, in shirtsleeves and trousers. The door-pounders were finally admitted, but they never found out (they never asked) that Přema's room had a separate entrance. They searched the apartment, they found nothing, the transmitter was in the wardrobe in the room with a separate entrance. But at the same time as they were half-heartedly searching, it was still before the age of exhausted executioners, curiosity got the better of Benda; he had no experience with the arrests that were to follow—nobody did, yet, at the time. While the arresting officers were looking in the usual hiding places at Přema's place, evidently hoping to find nothing, Benda read my moronic manifesto, mimeographed in about a hundred copies on a hand-cranked mimeograph machine that dated back to the Protectorate of *Böhmen und Mähren*, took the copies home (he lived just around the corner), threw them in the wood stove, set a match to them, and then gave in to his curiosity. He went and knocked on the door, but instead of the one-armed legionnaire, it was the arresting officers who opened.

"Is Přema Skočdopole home, please?"

"What do you want him for?"

And that was how it started. Old guard policemen, inherited from the *ancien regime*. They welcomed the opportunity to abandon the quarters of one who was obviously a rebel and to search those of one who was evidently innocent. Except that a routine glance inside the wood stove revealed the scorched but still legible copies of my manifesto (I hadn't believed in it much when I wrote it; I'd like to say it was the only text I ever wrote without total conviction; no, I'd be lying, there were others as well, later, but [almost] always in sponsorship mode, to help bring something worthwhile into the world. For that matter, treason, betraying one's homeland, or, in my case, betraying a political conviction—which in my case actually wasn't all that firm a conviction—is always a lesser sin than betrayal of a friend), and Benda was arrested, released (on bail? Maybe that still existed in those days.), then sentenced to eight months (prior to the age of exhausted executioners, a month was equivalent to a year), he got a postponement for starting to serve his sentence, but finally, the last day before he went inside, by then Přema was someplace (we didn't know where) in a DP camp, we spent the day at the swimming pool complex called Jericho (the work of some Jewish architect, it was the most beautiful place in the world, with a terrace for dancing, a veritable little Barrandov[47]; Irena used to go there sometimes, and I would have to keep going and jumping in the pool: fierce virginal longing inevitably creates a moistness, you can't help it, I had to keep my trunks wet all the time so Irena wouldn't notice the moistness; she had a fantastic cleavage in the decolletage of her bathing suit, I couldn't help myself and I was beyond help.), Benda stretched out despondently on the boards of the sun deck, mournfully contemplating his imminent incarceration (when he got out in May—he went in in September—we were on the sun deck again . . .) and the main thing he was afraid of was the humiliating shaving of his head (. . . and he said to me, "Soon as I was behind bars, first thing, I got busted in the snoot! I counted off wrong."—it was just the dawn of punchers in the nose and exhausted executioners), because he'd undergone that humiliation before, during the war, although that time it was voluntary, as far as anything we ever do is voluntary. His hair started getting thin, someone familiar with old wives' tales suggested he shave his head bald, a guaranteed cure. Benda submitted. In the hottest, most humid summer in Kostelec, he went around with a hat on, a hat deliberately too big so it could be pulled down to his ears, and that year he had even had to forego the pleasures of Jericho. As for movies—Benda was a passionate consumer of the poisons of Hollywood and other provenance—he would creep inside after the lights were out and flee outside as soon as THE END appeared on the screen; even at the factory (he was a lathe operator, but that didn't help him in court, he went on trial before the age of class origins, which two years later would save Ota from the noose) he went around with a cap on his head. And he went bald anyway. The grocer got two years, the correctional facility failed to correct him, and when he got out, he moved away from Kostelec.

"Why?"

"What do you mean, why, man, that's a stupid question," he explained to me years later, "It was the disgrace of having been in jail. I couldn't stand it." So badly was he burdened with uncorrected and bourgeois preconceptions, and of course, with the entrepreneurial diligence of the only genuine creators of successful economic systems, he retrained to become an electrician, last time I talked with him, during the time of dear old Saša, he had risen to the job of manager at Elektra, he wore a business suit and things were going well for him. Those swine, those opportunities for correction, the eternal, indestructible bourgeoisie, the vitality of the world (it strikes me that during the age of exhausted executioners, the bourgeoisie lost all the bad qualities described by classical greats of literature, and neither the age of executioners nor the age of *fizls* would allow the description of their good qualities, or else there were no greats of literature to describe them; it seems to me that the bad qualities were passed on to upper-level cadres, or those who would become cadres; a new class, but not a new bourgeoisie. That's a generalization, I know. Not all of them, but plenty. Certainly some.). And the one-armed legionnaire disassembled the transmitter, and by night they transported it across the neighboring roof piecemeal and threw it into the Ledhuje River. It was never found.

That's the kind of story it was. An ordinary story. And what led up to it? And what followed it? I don't think I can take you there. I haven't the patience. Long, long evenings on the promenade in Kostelec, endless evenings of chaste shyness, walking the desperate sidewalk past thousands of lovely girls. Přema never spoke to a single one of them. He was a product of the feminine mystique with its roots in the Victorian age of merchants and morality. He only yearned, he lacked my gift of gab, he lacked the grocer's unthinking pushiness, he just yearned, he smoked, he promenaded (to this day, that is, to the day I left that land, Benda, his peer and partner, still single, still walks that desperate promenade on Sundays after mass [but Father Meloun is gone, may he surely rest in peace]), from the savings bank to the Hotel Granada and back, taking a leak at the public toilet on the corner of the square, back to the savings bank, over to the Hotel Granada, back, then the street gradually emptied out, noon came and everyone went home for Sunday dinner. Benda never left that desert, not even after he turned fifty.

Přema left it. We used to promenade like that every day, late into the night. Often with Rosťa, the painter, long before any of us had ever heard of Tolkien, Rosťa invented a nonexistent realm with a nonexistent language inhabited by nonexistent hobbits, he wrote its history, drew its maps—all that is gone, now. Even the bold, detailed plans for catching girls in the net of youthful raunchiness (innocent raunchiness: seeking no more than to cop a feel, a game of kissy-face, terribly fumbling approaches to intercourse, terribly difficult purchases of rubbers, "Have you got—um, a toothbrush?" "Have you got—er, toothpaste?" "Hey, I'll give you a crown if you'll run down to the drugstore and buy me, I've written it down here for you on this piece of paper." The malicious druggist sold the kid a toothbrush to bring me), for catching the chaste Irena and the even chaster Marie. I described it in *The Swell Season*, how, betraying a friendship (betrayal of a friend doesn't count when you make a play for his girl, platonic as relationships were during those high school days), I used to walk Rosťa's Marie home

from her piano lesson late in the evening and how I filled
the fragrant air of summer and winter nights in Kostelec
with an interminable cascade of words, babbling poems in
prose, so much better than the rhymed ones I hunted and
pecked out on my typewriter at home; Marie listened, she
was a beautiful but unattainable, strawberry sweet but unattainable girl (now she has a daughter, another strawberry), a
very Catholic girl, but even Catholic girls like to hear nice
things about themselves, "Oh, Danny-boy, you're kidding
me," was her refrain, I also used to put that beautiful and oh,
so truthful youthful prattle in, yes, pink letters (I wonder
where they are? How many of the girls in Kostelec had a
good giggle over them? I wonder if Marie's strawberry
daughter gets to giggle over them too?) that I sent off by
mail. I couldn't care less that she was Rosťa's. She was
everybody's. She belongs to the whole world.

But I've written stories about all that, and this is a different story. And yet: I never will totally and unequivocally
succeed at writing it, but for me, Marie is a portrait that Mr.
Řeřicha could have painted if Rembrandt had painted in the
background for him. The background is dark, Marie in a
dazzling pool of light, her full pink-red lips like a strawberry
in a dazzling white face (Marie was fair; a stirringly fair
lovely blonde). The municipal theater, where the drama of
The Bass Saxophone was played out (it really was played out,
that is not fiction), a beautiful Edwardian building, we knew
how to get backstage without paying and we got to watch
touring companies from the fly gallery (one time Benda
thought he was being smart and hid behind a set, they were
putting on some conversation piece, its main claim to fame

was the fact that the heroine had to appear on stage in a different outfit every five minutes. The only way this feat could be accomplished, technically, was that underneath it all she wore only hose and a garter belt and panties—no bra, because some of the outfits were evening gowns with low cut backs, bare down to the waist—and so every five minutes she would amble easily over to the exit, and once backstage, the amble [what's an amble?] would switch into a madly accelerated striptease, she'd yank off one outfit, pull on the next one that was laid out for her on a sofa backstage; there was no wardrobe mistress, it was just a poor road company. And the first time she ambled offstage and started yanking off her clothes, she glanced back into the darkness, and noticed a round face, peering out from among the ropes: it was Benda's face, topped off by the large hat pulled down to this ears on account of the shaved head. Well, the show must go on, and so she just stuck her tongue out at him, the way they used to do in those days, and in the course of the first act—the play only had two—allowed him the pleasure of viewing her very lovely breasts a total of ten times. During the intermission, Benda tried to slip away, but she caught him, dragged him into her dressing room and presented him, with malice aforethought, with a complimentary ticket to the proscenium loge, where for the first and last time during his medical treatment Benda removed the hat from his shaven head in public, and sat there, his bald head gleaming in the reflected light from the stage. After the performance, she went out for a drink with him, but her partner—who was also apparently her lover—was there as well, nothing came of it, it just sort of fizzled. That was as

close as the dear innocent from the promenade ever got to a
female breast. "Weren't you wet?" asked the pushy grocer.
"You bet I was," admitted the virtuous Benda, blushing.)
But that afternoon, I was only backstage because our jazz
band was rehearsing downstairs in the wine bar, and someone said that the Hron Singers were rehearsing onstage for
an evening performance, with a guest appearance by Eduard
Haken.[48] I was there with Benno and Lexa merely out of
idle curiosity, I was totally indifferent to choral groups and
opera, my own music blared with the wail of Lunceford-
type saxophones. But even as we were climbing the spiral
staircase, a melody sounded, a Lunceford-type melody, it
seemed to me to actually swing, a lovely, unforgettable tune
(my introduction to Dvořák; that was how I realized that
the greatest art in music, or maybe the prime fundamental
art, is the classical beauty of bare, unadorned melody),
"White blossoms all along the road, along the road all over,"[49]
sang the choir of girl's voices, lovely beyond imagining (it
was probably both male and female voices, but at that age I
always heard nothing but the female voices, that is, in a
choir, I automatically tuned the others out) and in it, with
it, against it, in the most delicious dialectic (counterpoint;
old Maestro Dvořák, as they refer to him here, possibly
never encountered the word *dialectic* in all his life; certainly
not in anything but the classical sense), Haken's splendid
voice singing harmony, like the voice of a velvet-covered
oak tree, *"Water lilies, blossoms white, will be your sad companion"*—we walked out of the stairwell and the picture before
me was that Řeřicha painting on the Rembrandt background, standing out from the deep darkness of the flies, the

brightly illuminated lagoon of the girl's choir flanking the tall figure of the operatic basso, and in the middle of that lagoon, golden locks (probably coiffed in some period coiffure, Marie was always careful about how she looked) framing the white pool that was Marie's face, with the lovely girlish strawberry mouth of sixteen-year-old pubescence, which from that time forward was my sole aesthetic. *"Do not wait and tarry, lad, and hasten to your lover,"* I tarried not, I hastened, but I never did arrive; I am an artist, sometimes an inferior one, mostly mediocre, occasionally perhaps a really good one, but by inner disposition an artist, hence a virgin; no artist has ever lost the virginity of that vision, that youthful strawberry pout in the alabaster of the girlish countenance, that immaculate lily of youth; *"When you come back by this way, the roses will be blooming red,"* but no: they were being hanged. There is no blood, they just turn green, the tongue slips out, swells, turns black, then they get a diabolical erection, as if to confirm the old tales about the reason for the sacrifices of the Black Mass. One soldier (that is: one guard) of the revolution thought up his idea of a revolutionary joke: occasionally he would tell them, "Get ready. Today is execution day." He'd give them shaving brushes and straight razors, let them shave, let them contemplate in bodily terror the final affairs of the soul, the final affairs of man, whereupon he would tell them, the execution is postponed till tomorrow. The revolutionary wit of one of the revolution's jailers who had *"that beautiful detachment and devotion to stern justice of men dealing in death without being in any danger of it."*[50] Hemingway: this is the crux of his writing, a precisely formulated essential truth of our century: if he had

written nothing else, he would still remain as much a part of
literature as Shakespeare (whose greatness is also in a few
such fundamental formulations, not in the tedious plots of
his pointless plays). It stayed with me from the days of the
Protectorate, and was confirmed by the succession of ruth-
less men, and later painfully gutless ones, led by K.H. Frank,
first liquidating Lidice, later, beneath the gallows, longing to
go to the Balearic Islands, followed by mobs crying "Hang
them! Hang them!" led by the poet Skála (*"to dogs, a dog's
death"*),[51] who after a brief period of protest once again lost
his guts in (reputedly good) rhymes (I have nothing against
gutlessness, which is human, but what revolts me is dealing
with death without being in any danger of it, which is
inhuman, and which has been the hallmark of Czech poets,
humanistic authoresses and former Gestapo agents, increasingly strident as they tried with their shrillness to escape the
prospect of their own gallows). And then, one day, they
were lathering up in earnest.

Such are the disparate human situations of our world.
That revolutionary guard? Two possibilities. Either they dis-
missed him for so-called "unsanctioned methods," and he is
now working in some more mundane job, certainly, as they
say over there, he remains a part of the hardy core of the
Party (the legendary Kohoutek—described by London[52]—
was behind bars for a year for using such methods, and immediately upon his release was named to a high post with
the Czechoslovak Pavilion at the Brussels Expo of 1958,
which damaged the careers of so many artists who took part
in it),[53] or else they never did dismiss him, he rose to captain, he interrogates (punctiliously) the Vaculíks of this

world,[54] and receives the petty reports of the petty informers of this age of petty *fizls*.

For this is indeed the age of petty *fizls* and snitches, they
even ducked under the surface of the river that flowed
through the year 1968. Oh, how much I'd prefer to stay
with the light glowing out of the darkness, with Marie in
that long-gone year when I was seventeen, but moments of
pure, essential beauty are rare—as perhaps they should be.
She is painted on a canvas that is far too sheer, the consist-
ency of gossamer, delicate, fragile. Rosťa, the painter, cap-
tured her. His best painting was of Marie. But because I
loved that painting, in May of 1945, when I was editor of
the Youth Union magazine (in those days, the Union had
not yet become an affiliate of the Party),[55] called *Youth Has
Its Say, Northeast*, I published a black-and-white reproduc-
tion of it in the very first issue, and I titled it, not Marie, but
Idea. And I accompanied it with an article about Art, which,
in my opinion, rests in Beauty, yes, both capitalized. Soon
there came a disagreeable letter from Czechoslovak Youth
Union (CYU) headquarters in Prague. On the carpet, I
stood corrected, in that early summer of 1945: Art does not
rest in Beauty, but in its reflection of Class. Up till then, the
only association I had had for the word *class* was class register.[56] That and nothing else. They also enlightened me
about Class Struggle, and unless I'm mistaken, also about the
Dictatorship of the Proletariat. Me, who had just lived
through one dictatorship, one that banned jazz; me, whose
head contained one Idea with two names: Irena and Marie
(four, actually: the other two were entirely incorporeal:
mere light images projected on a screen: Judy and Deanna).

I returned to Kostelec. All right then, no more about Marie. About the age of *fizls*, about one of their number.

Back to my story. Of course, I could fabricate, embellish, dramatize, add dialogue. That is a matter of my craft (sometimes, when I read the critics, I have the feeling that I am the only one who does not underrate them). But for the substance of this text, the only thing that is important about this story is its conclusion and not the narrative effects between beginning and end, and I hope to find in that conclusion some small certainty in the sea of my uncertainty. I could embellish the bare, paradigmatic story of that age with a spell cast of atmosphere, entirely fictitious dialogue (transposed, in fact, to the level of literary prose from my subconscious recollections of penny dreadfuls I had read) just as I could transpose myself into the person of the strawberry Marie, for examples of this are numerous indeed, familiar and abiding in the subconscious, human beings are an eternal reprise performed from a common libretto, except that, as folk wisdom (ever ribald, yes, ever ribald, at least in Christendom where it was frowned upon, perhaps not so in the lands of more erotic gods) would have it, the ones have a crack down there while the others have an appendage; such a transposition would again be no more than a transmutation, taking advantage of our natural androgyny. The strawberry Marie, however, was and will always remain no more than a picture, a beauty that is only skin deep, the whole lovely world of Kostelec (including the ugly external world) is no more than skin deep, I can't see beneath the skin, I can't see beneath anyone's skin so I am always on the outside looking in. Only narrative and dialogue and first person singular (certainly, now and then the third person singular, but then the Third Person is just borrowing the eyes of the First Person; not consistently, though—unfortunately [unfortunately?]—a person learns technique, and unlearns the intensity of life [and hence of his work]), *Tankáč*, as they nicknamed my novel *The Tank Corps*, that progeny of despair and helplessness, in the normalized People's Army, if I can believe what they wrote me on unsigned postcards (not that I like that kind of sobriquet but it does indicate a brief moment of mortal immortality, doesn't it? When the unknown readers for whom it was written, after all, take the title of the book and make it into a new slang word; dare I hope for at least a moment, with Čapek,[57] that perhaps I have *"written a novel, every copy of which circulates from hand to hand. . .",* hands marked by *"a hard life, until . . . all the copies lose their title pages and no one . . . knows who the author is. In fact, knowing it is unnecessary, since everyone has found himself in it"?* Here is an excerpt from an anonymous card: *"It goes from hand to hand, tattered paperbacks retyped as* samizdats, *and passed around in chapter by chapter. You won't find a barracks where there isn't a copy of* The Tank Corps, *no matter how the* politruks[58] *fume and toss the guys caught reading it into the hole, it's no use, the barracks are crawling with copies of it. Division and Company clerks and people in accounting recopy passages from* Tankáč *and even some higher officers have been caught with this 'trash' in their pockets."*), anyway, *Tankáč* is a report, albeit of course an inconsistent one, on the thoughts of several persons that I can't vouch for. But I was young, I had no skills (no technical ones, maybe some life skills), untutored, unknowing, but I remember my despair at the Martinovka

Chalet in the Krkonoše Mountains, sitting on a moldering boulder, overwhelmed by the fragrance of the dwarf pines, alone (Lizetka had other guys), writing the Fučík Medal chapter, the mountains splendid, mountains lost to you even before you can appreciate them (I lacked Irena's gift of a consummate love of Nature; I preferred people, but they were hard to get close to, so I used to walk in the mountains, alone, the poetry of Nature, the fragrances and the dusky light of the mountains before an approaching rain, the mists and the rows of mountain peaks stretching out one behind the other like on a theatrical backdrop, but because I [probably] never could stand [Why? I don't know. Probably, to be honest, because I lacked them myself.] those kinds of consummate, orthodox and broadly accepted predilections and passions, I used to shock the ladies of the Falcon with cynical remarks exalting the virtues of night clubs over those of the woods of Kostelec.), it was to be a great novel, like the proverbial and famous Great American Novel, which of course I never will write, not just for a lack of talent, but because no one will ever write it; it's an inner paradigm that we have, the luminous inner world in which the alchemy of thought transforms the real outer world, its radiant moments placed like glass jewels in the velvet black sky above the manger; that is, the inner paradigm which we then try to transform into words, into an extravagant product (which all dictatorships—otherwise venerating extravagance when applied to the select few—perceive as threatening) made of words, and of course, the transmutation is always imperfect, we cringe with despair and shame over the grotesque and flickering caricature of that inner radiance. Back in the desk drawer, back to what is known as the process of maturation. The scene from the radiant world goes dim, replaced in your mind (in your soul? Ah, if only I could believe in a soul, but the world appears to me as so devastatingly chemical.) by other radiant scenes. That particular one grows dim in the desk drawer; after a while you pull it open, after a year, two, you've forgotten that specific radiance, and the text, that extravagance, suddenly shines out at you (if you were lucky, that is, if you were what they call inspired as you stitched the thread of ink into that extravagant consumer product), the strawberry Marie on Mr. Řeřicha's bonbon figural painting in the Rembrandt frame glows because the inner paradigm has dimmed and the artifact meets the eye, and comes back to radiant life, a corrected, adapted thing, extravagantly embroidered out of words. Anyway: fresh out of the army, I was getting ready to write the Great Novel, The Life of Danny in the Big City of Prague, but the Life of Danny in those days was far too intense and I was incapable of embroidering its complexities (I recall: "See the window? At night? There's a light on in the room. There are some people moving around in there. The scene is mute. Like fish in an aquarium. Describe it! Describe it so it happens! Happens! But it HAPPENS!" said Lizetka, herself a sorry victim of the illness I call the extravagance of words), and so I concocted—as a mere prologue to the novel—an encounter, a collision with what is known as life, with what the so-called People call basic military service, just a fragment. Now, years later, perhaps I can see the virtue of this fragment: maybe what Henry Miller said applies to it (but it's probably my conceit; no: it's that I'm afraid of dying, no, not of

dying, but of the realization that when I die, I will be dead.
So maybe it is not—certainly not—conceit, but immodesty.
I want more than I have coming to me. I probably deserve
to be dead while I'm still alive. Unless that in itself is conceit; I am more alive now than most, and I'm not grateful.
So it's ingratitude. *Mea culpa. Deus, ne me relinquis.*): *"And
when you show me a man who expresses himself perfectly I will not
say that he is not great, but I will say that I am unattracted . . . I
run with joy to the great and imperfect ones, their confusion nour-
ishes me, their stuttering is like divine music to my ears . . . today
more than ever a book should be sought after even if it has only one
great page in it: we must search for fragments, splinters, toenails,
anything that has ore in it, anything that is capable of resuscitating
body and soul."*[59] For that's the way it was, because of course
it wasn't that way, it wasn't, because nobody, not me nor
anyone else, could penetrate the complexity of Private
Bamza or Captain Matka, each of us can penetrate only our
own complexities (I'm not saying understand them; just
penetrate and report on them, in cabalese to draft a rough
news item, censored by the publisher from his office in your
mind), the difference is in that neither Private Bamza nor
Captain Matka will ever file a report from their interior, not
even in cabalese. Why then, if we don't know how to do
more than transpose our own interior into a stylized pen-
and-ink sketch of an interior, not even a photograph (much
less reality), at best no more than a sketch: the impression of
spatters, the rough outlines of a cubist stylization—why then
create the misty outlines of other people's interiors using the
analogy of the read and the internal (in part they turn out to
be drivel: there is too much *Dichtung* and too little *Wahrheit*

even in the external. Or is it the other way around? The only thing that is certain is that nothing is pure *Dichtung* nor pure *Wahrheit*.). Perhaps it is that Truth is truer than truth, but only because the uncertainty of that statement seems to correspond more to the radiant uncertainty of the inner models of reality of those who read. Except: that what if it is only what is left of reality in the inner model that is the truth, the substance, the idea, the quintessential, and everything else is nothing but irrelevant incidentals. So that: Certainly. Bamza, Private Bamza never talked in such crystalline terms. But talk he did. The way he talks in my novel is his quintessence. I couldn't see into the cavern inside him. What I would be able to present as the quintessence of the cavern would be just an analogy. Not the *Ding an Sich*, which of course is the soldier himself, the actual strawberry Marie: perhaps the radiant model transposed into an extravagant product made of words.

And so I don't know anything about the *Ding*, I merely know its quintessence. Which is: a dazzling little pool, lily cheeks, a golden frame of hair. That radiant Sunday, the little blue coat with its (then stylish) hood, bordered with fake fur in a V shape (V for Victory, or, as the Nazis adopted it for their own, *fau für fiktoria*). The strawberry pout. And then, another bit of Rembrandtiana in Prague, a dance in the Slavonic Hall, her little knees in shiny nylon, I didn't know why she had come, not even Rosťa knew, we just found out she was there, the small-town beauty in the Big City of Prague, she danced for one evening, never a word about why she was here, then she left, she married. All that against the backdrop of the dark autumn night in Prague. No, I know. The quintessence is her daughter, but to me, to Rosťa, to the other girl-watchers on the promenade, it was those few shorthand symbols that represented her (or that were her): the crown of her hair, *fau für fiktoria*, and the heavy ribbed stockings she used to wear back home. Popular opinion to the contrary notwithstanding, we did not undress them with the eyes we lived by. On the contrary. It was those eyes that dressed them in that immortal little coat, in ribbed stockings. The strawberry pout on the Řeřicha painting far outstripped fantasies of boobs and pubes: in fact, there never really were any. The coat was more fantastic (the leather patches on Irena's little backside between sandstone cliffs). That (perhaps) is what girls like that signify in this world: their meaning is in their youth, it is their youth that entices us to a reprise (their youth, not their boobs), everything else is unfortunately nothing but an epilogue; sometimes not a bad one, but certainly an epilogue. Their charms are difficult and complex, all intertwined with the woes of the world, while the hierarchy of relevance remains unclear; but in youth, there is the radiance of the lagoon of the countenance, the strawberry of the lips, spotlighted against the Rembrandtesque darkness of time.

Anyway, just a paradigmatic tale: it started in the refugee camp on Sicily, he was there for a year, and then another year, because he never was good at knowing his way around. Then, maybe three, four years after the night I tried in vain to connect, not in order to do battle (I'm not that kind of a fighter) but in order to confirm a friendship; I didn't want to fight, Benno, fat and jolly, had almost convinced me, and I always inclined towards Utopia, my soul wanted Utopia. I was saved by—what? My bourgeois father's fears? His (perhaps instinctive, certainly not purely rational) mistrust? Be that as it may: I wanted Utopia. Truly, it's not to my credit, no virtue, no conscious effort, it's just the way I am, I don't fight for myself, for my own benefit, it certainly looks as if I do, but when I do fight on my own behalf, it isn't at the expense of others; I would like it if I didn't have to; socialism— unsullied since it doesn't exist under that name, sullied like a beggar's penny—ought to (could if it could; perhaps it can if it proves able to) make it possible. Anyway, so I wanted Utopia, but those sentences: Jarmila Ebenová, born 1932, fifteen years; Jiří Kořínek, born 1933, twenty years, Dagmar Želivská, born 1932, ten years, all that in 1950, former Boy Scout leaders found guilty of organizing illegal Boy Scout troops for the benefit of the Vatican. Dr. Milada Horáková,[60] sentenced to death for grand treason (that horrible, Stalinist, maybe Leninist, what do I know, Orwellianism, because what had she betrayed? Klement Gottwald's republic was a hostile state; she was not the one to declare enmity, it was Gottwald. His Party. Is it possible to betray an enemy? He believed in enmity, in society as a struggle to the death— *"We travel to Moscow to learn how to wring your necks"*[61]—while she believed, along with Čapek, in ordinary decent people. If only they had simply killed her, the classical revolutionary murder which unfortunately exists only in literature: Greene: *"You're a danger. That's why we kill you. I have nothing against you, you understand, as a man."*[62] Perhaps it did exist in France's terror machine: "I'm killing you because you're an aristocrat." But why douse it with the stinking sauce of pseudo-legality? Why the nauseating stench of

ideological pseudo-justice and the pretense that was a national pseudo-indignation? A new category of newspeak:
Betraying the Enemy?), they were what saved me, they sus-
tained my common sense. See, I wanted free medicine and
doctors too (free: of course, they were paid for through
compulsory insurance, that IS Christian. Love your neighbor. You may not need help, but there are always those who
do), I wanted security in my old age too (again: through
compulsory insurance, that is, not just for the prudent, the
fortunate, the diligent), I also wanted for hands and minds
that lived by work never to be unemployed again. But I
took it literally: scientifically. Betraying the Enemy is a mys-
tical concept, I am not a mystic, I never will be, not this kind
of a mystic. Strawberry pout, oh yes. A metaphor. But not
Betraying the Enemy. An oxymoron. Not an oxymoron.
Pure cynical newspeak. And also, not twenty years in a concentration camp just because at nineteen, someone still held
one opinion the way someone else held another (one being
bad, reactionary, criminal; the other being right, progressive,
favored in the eyes of the Party [God]), while a third someone at nineteen didn't even believe in one or the other, but
in the convenient wisdom of wearing a mask, and the fool-
ishness of any other belief, and yet a fourth, like me, didn't
believe, didn't know, wasn't certain, abstained from belief
not out of cowardice (or at least not primarily out of cowardice), but because he just didn't know. So that's what saved
me. Salvation of the individual, purchased by centuries that
were the sum of accumulated years lived by those girls
and guys who believed in one thing (not in the other, and
not only wisely; and not with uncertainty), in the places

with names that (in me, at least) evoke the lamentation of Bucharest's Cantor Katz: Auschwitz, Maidaneck, Treblinka, Bitýz, Rovnost, Příbram, Jáchymov . . .

So then: maybe three, four years later, a postcard from Algiers:

Greetings from Algiers,
             Your Old Buddy P.

Then for a long time, nothing. I didn't connect Algiers and the first war in Vietnam (what did they call it then? Indochina?), and about a year later, a postcard with an Italian stamp:

Greetings from Sicily,
             Your Old Buddy.

I didn't connect anything, I didn't know (I never knew much of anything in life) that there were camps where they detain people stripped bare. Stripped of passports, uniforms, identity cards, for (what they saw as) good reasons: former SS-men who succeeded in slipping away from their conquerors[63]; former members of the Ustashi militia; men (the most miserable of all) formerly of Vlasov's army; and also those who concealed themselves among the men who were stripped bare, hired assassins who were fleeing Interpol (or whatever it was called in those days). And also the ones who didn't know their way around Europe and instead of signing an immigration visa application form to the sweet new world, ended up signing another kind of form: Marseille,

army camps in the oases of North Africa, troop ships, Indochina. It wasn't until years later that I found out the details of
this adventure novel: how he jumped ship, swam to shore,
traded his good army boots (around his neck) for civilian
clothes, but they caught him, he was mute, though, spoke
no Spanish, spoke no German (he'd refused to learn it for
patriotic reasons in his youth in the Protectorate of *Böhmen
und Mähren*), and instead of Indochina, it was the camp on
Sicily. There he lived among SS-men and Ustashists and
common foul murderers (as did the grocer, and Benda, except elsewhere) and among the few who got themselves
blown by the winds of incredible destiny to some obscure
little spot on the globe (what is my reader Evžena Čtvrtková
doing on the Freedom Islands? How in God's name did she
get there?). After that, nothing for a long time, and then a
letter from Australia.

> *Greetings from Sydney,*
> > *Your Old Buddy.*

Years flew by, as they always do; with the incredible
speed of light. Then a photo: Your Old Buddy. On a farm.
In Australia, though. He had no wife. Nearest neighbor
three hundred miles away, and he was alone. He battled the
rabbits. In the end he sold the farm, his mother in Kostelec
told me he couldn't take the solitude, and back to factory
work, in Sydney, in Melbourne, in some other city.

Yes, I could write a novel. ("His life," they say "is a veritable novel. But," they say, "if you wrote it, nobody would
believe it.") But I won't. It's not something I lived, I just

lived the postcards. *"Your Old Buddy"* (a reflex according to Pavlov: it always evoked the image of Kostelec, its promenade, its secondary school, old buddies, I've lived what most of them have lived. No foreign legion, it's true, but: other stuff. I'm not saying it was any worse. But there are two kinds of danger: the danger faced by a toreador or a soldier, and the danger of an animal in a trap. Both might die, and might not. But for the toreador and the soldier, it also depends at least a little bit on whether he defends himself. For the animal it is strictly a matter of the mercy or the cruelty of the one who set the trap. The animal can defend itself too, of course, like the soldier and the toreador, but it's two different kinds of courage: one kind with a chance, the other without. The other, I believe, is the greater. That's where I think General Eliáš[64] was, in the trap that was the Protectorate of *Böhmen und Mähren*, and so he was braver than the partisans who risked their lives in the Tatra woods. His situation, again, was paradigmatic for our fragrant land. The situation of the cage they catch you in. The one they've caught so many of them in.). Like Jarka, another old friend who came to me in Prague. I once loved him so much that the wisdom of this silly age might have called it a homosexual tendency, repressed but sublimated into a projection of a curious religious notion. Jarka took his religion classes in the Czechoslovak denomination, whereas I, at that time still a profound believer—although I think that by then, my faith had long since encompassed a grain of doubt: at the age of nine I believed in dinosaurs, that is, in a different history of the world than the biblical one; but when I confessed this fallacy—never ceasing to believe it—to Father Meloun in

the cold confessional (I had fourteen sins on a scrap of paper,
Bert Grym only had four. I saw myself as only a step removed from Cain) at my first Holy Confession, but the
Reverend Father told me, "That's not an article of the Faith.
It's not something you need to confess." I accepted that as a
mystery of the Faith, and I felt better. Absolved of my sins,
with mixed feelings (I knew I ought to be experiencing the
bliss of God's Sacramental Grace, but I wasn't altogether sure
that was what I was experiencing.), I walked home in the
sunny afternoon, and at home, automatically, impulsively,
out of childish habit, I lied: it was some kind of an infantile,
unnecessary lie, I don't even recall what about. I realized it
right away. And with my First Communion the very next
day. A dreamless, sleepless night—my first, although there
would be many more in my life—and in the morning, no
breakfast, to St. Michael's, line up with little girls in white
and little boys in their Sunday best, and the hand of Father
Meloun starts towards me with that odd gesture, holy calisthenics, pudgy fingers dipping into the golden chalice and
out of the golden chalice, delicately grasping the white
wafer, the round white body of Christ the Lord, placing it
deliberately on one little girl's stuck-out tongue (stuck out
all the way to her chin, in spite of Father Meloun's earlier
admonition: "See to it that you just poke the tip of your
tongue out of your mouth. So you're not sticking your
tongue out at me!" he waggled a pudgy index finger at us
amiably), the little girl, awestruck, upset, her long girlie
tongue almost touching the ribbon under her chin, the host
sticks and the little girl flips tongue and host inside her
mouth like an anteater would, closes her mouth and bows

her head to the ribbon, beating her tiny chest in hollow high C; beside her a little boy with his tongue stuck out, and a second and a third, and another little girl, inevitably, instead of Sacramental Grace I feel the approach of the Sin of Sacrilege, acrid with the stink of Hell, and the white wafer hangs above me, my eyes are wide, I see it double, "Open your mouth," I hear Father Meloun, I open it but I don't put out my tongue, "Father, I sinned . . . since my Confession . . ." I am close to fainting in panic that they will banish me from the church without having swallowed the round body of Christ, that I will have to repent all over again—alone—and not explain why to anyone; Bert would expose me, "He had fourteen sins! Fourteen! That's too many! Ordinary penance wasn't enough. So Father Meloun wouldn't let him take his First Communion!" And then, blessed deliverance, the divine goodness of that tall, peasant of a man, his head so like the melon that named him: "In your mind, say: 'Lord God, I truly and profoundly regret my sin'!" "Lord God I truly and profoundly regret my sin," I said in my mind, and I truly and profoundly did. "Open your mouth!" Against my will, my tongue flew down towards my vest, I felt the wafer stick to it, like an anteater I pulled Christ into my mouth, pounded my chest, Christ got soggy, curled up, I swallowed, and the bliss that followed was psychologically logical: the resolution of a traumatic situation.

So I was very much a believer. And I did love Jarka, who was my math tutor, and whose father had a small farm. At one point, I was struck by his appalling prospect in the afterlife. He didn't have a chance, he was aware of the existence of the Catholic Church and yet he still believed in another faith. He would surely end up in Hell, while I might end up in Heaven. I knew, with far more certainty than I felt the Sacramental Grace of God, that there would be no bliss in Heaven without Jarka. No, I didn't have the courage to say I'd rather go to Hell with Jarka. The image of Hell I believed in was like the one depicted by Joyce. The day turned black, misery and despair as only a child, and then perhaps old age, can know. The absence of Jarka in my Heaven would not be redeemed even by the presence of God.

In time we became and remained (old) buddies. "Man, I need some advice," he said to me that day in my Prague apartment with the lovely Baroque view of St. Margaret's (*basilica minor*; I don't know what that means in church terminology, but it has the sweet sound of youth, intimacy; minor, like the strawberry Marie).

"What's up?"

"What's up," said Jarka, "is my being in trouble."

"Again?" I wondered, because that was a riot, he'd been in trouble before: he'd come to me like this in my apartment with the view of the lovely Margaret—no, wait, it was when I was subletting from the widow Ledvinová, a long time before—completely beside himself because he had kept something from his wife, and with superhuman effort, he had borne the burden of clandestine child support, four hundred a month to the other mother, a woman of character who didn't betray him, but needed the four hundred a month. How, under socialism, does one earn an extra four hundred a month on top of a fixed wage (a figure his wife was intimately familiar with)? "How do you do it?" I had asked the completely exhausted Jarka, and the completely exhausted Jarka had explained that he moonlighted as a bookkeeper for three manufacturing cooperatives but told his wife it was just one, and that he also helped out as a bartender at country dances in his native village, but told his wife he was going there to visit with his mother, the completely exhausted Jarka and this Sisyphean boulder, on account of a few ludicrous moves, a few panting calisthenics, a few moments of rapture. He had shouldered that boulder for eighteen years until the kid came of age (the kid turned out to be a lovely strawberry) and by the grace of God plus his own diligence plus the single mother's strength of character (and later that of her spouse, who had found the money useful), Jarka's wife had never found out. Later on, of course, it was easier: he didn't tell her about two subsequent raises in pay, which enabled him to quit keeping books for one of the co-ops.

And yet—*nihil humani a me*, in spite of the fact that they'd say that if I wrote it, nobody would believe it—Jarka didn't let up. He was a chronic stud, straight out of Kundera, a veritable jackhammer, I'm not certain just when he started hammering but it must have been, good God, back in the sixth grade, because it wasn't until grade nine that I figured out why he had cracked up when as sixth graders, walking past the familiar convex OLLA RUBBER!!? ad in Mr. Černoch's drugstore window, which I'd been wondering about for a long time, probably on account of the question mark, because I usually paid no attention to advertisements, and I remarked pensively, "Y'know, I'd really like to know what OLLA RUBBER!!? means," and Jarka nearly bust a gut laughing, but he would never divulge the secret of the ad to me. And by that time, I was in love with girls already, Ichka, the one I would help administer an artificial pneumothorax to, ten years later. The way I found out about it all was the way most children of the bourgeoisie did, since at home, they were kept in the dark about these things: I read it on the wall of the boys' toilet at the Sokol Theatre. It was right there, in the movie house that I experienced the revelation of maturity, and because this is not a novel, where such things are not discussed, at least so say the righteous sages (just as we know that Anna Karenina must have used the toilet, and yet we won't find a single mention of it in Leo Nikolayevich's novel, the word is never so much as mentioned, even though it is a commonly used one), so because this isn't a novel but a patho-biography, I will quote the graffiti verbatim:

Prick in cunt makes baby!

A milestone on the way to maturity. I can't help it, that's what was scrawled there, among all the usual doggerel, and that's how I found out. At the time, though, it didn't sink in somehow, maybe I'd never encountered a milestone before, it didn't move me forward one little bit. That wasn't what girls meant to me, not Irena, not Marie. I was apparently a little backward. Sure, I begged for it. But if I'd gotten what I was begging for, my knowledge of what to do with Ichka would have been pure theory. That was what our (my?) wonderful youth was like in that wonderful town of Kostelec.

Of course, Jarka knew what the question mark was all about. Jarka the jackhammer hammered and hammered, and then there he was a second time at my place, sitting there beside the window that opened out onto the minor basilica, and he said, "No, not THAT kind of trouble again. This time it's worse trouble."

The only possible alternative that occurred to me that could have been worse than extramarital paternity was venereal disease. Dr. Eichler used to threaten us with it whenever the curriculum called for instruction on sex; so in my mind, sex was not associated with plums like Marie or Irena, but with the terrible ailments one could pick up at a place like The Bend in the Road. That was what made me turn tail and flee like a coward the time all of the guys in the band went there together about a year after the doctor had enlightened us. One prostitute came outside, grabbed Lexa, and me, I took off. As I recall, Lexa didn't catch any disease. In fact, later on, he even survived the notorious Bitýz concentration camp.

"I've got a friend who's a doctor," I consoled Jarka, but it turned out that a doctor wasn't what he needed at all. The thing was, he had gone on a business trip to Zelený Hradec, everything had been arranged and set, his colleague (female, married) had taken a separate room, indeed, in those days of the exhausted executioners, that was the way one sinned against the catechism: ten minutes after she signed in at the reception desk, Jarka picked up the key to his room, but went right upstairs to hers, that was how extramarital affairs were conducted in that age of exhausted executioners and the housing crisis. Then came a brief round of the same ludicrous calisthenics that once before had earned him eighteen years of Sisyphean labor, and as the acoustic aspect of this physical exertion was about to culminate, it occurred to him

that the banging on the hotel room door was probably that
of an indiscreet hotel guest, irritated by the noise. He was
soon disabused of this misapprehension: "Open up! Police!"
There ensued a reverse striptease, and the entry of two men
demanding identification. They were civil, they were cool,
they were matter-of-fact, the only comment they made
(upon examining Jarka's ID), was, "You're supposed to be in
room twelve, Comrade!" They left, as did all desire for calisthenics. The next two weeks Jarka stewed in his own juices,
then came a telephone call, followed by a meeting with the
two men in a small office. A discourse on the classic theory
of *fízldom*: "We're not interested in reactionaries. Or pro-
gressives. The ones we're interested in are the ambivalent,
the indecisive, the unreliable ones. All we're asking of you is
to contribute to our way of helping them. We can't give
them any effective help if we don't know them well enough,
if we don't have enough information about them." A classical theory of modern pedagogy. Followed by the equally
classical: "You have a week to think it over. Of course, if
you're not interested, your wife may be interested in what
you were doing two weeks ago in a hotel room with someone else's wife."

"Man, what'll I do?" Jarka asked (classically). It wasn't
until later (things always occur to me later) that it dawned
on me what overwhelming evidence of our friendship it
was, his confiding in me, and not incidentally, violating
his solemn oath ("Sign here that you swear you won't tell
anybody about what we've talked about."). Of course, I
couldn't advise him to accept their offer, and of course he
didn't expect me to. I could see only three possibilities.

"Tell your wife. It's a bad scene, but then they won't have anything on you."

"I can't!" exclaimed Jarka, totally drained. Of course he couldn't, it dawned on me, fourteen years (at the time) of secretly rolling the boulder of child-support uphill would have been all for naught.

"Yeah, well, okay," I said.

"What can they do to me?" he asked.

"Hard to tell. Probably nothing worse than telling your wife. And telling her about the other, too. They must know about it, they're probably saving it for a rainy day, and the rain clouds are gathering."

Jarka turned pale, his yellowed fingers (a heavy smoker, he always stank of smoke from a distance, and yet, girls were all over him, even though his kisses must have tasted like a drink of water from a bar-top ashtray) shook so hard his burning cigarette slipped to the floor, whereupon he formulated a bit of classical pragmatism: "Either they won't do anything, I bet they try this on a lot of people, and if you wimp out, you're in shit. Or else they'll tell the wife"—the retrieved cigarette resumed its trembling—"and that will be the total end of me"—now the cigarette was shaking uncontrollably. (I never could understand why so intense a fear of his wife: she was such a nice, pretty hospital nurse. I'd have said she probably wasn't all that saintly herself. The only explanation could be that he loved her that much, and he didn't want to cause her pain, but given the extent of his philandering, that didn't seem very probable either. Still, what other explanation was there?) "I even considered signing it for them and then giving them false

reports, good ones about good people and ratting on Party
swine. But they'd probably figure that out, and then they'd
still go to the wife." What was left of his cigarette butt fell
out of his fingers again, and he picked it up and relit it.
With shaking fingers, he went to stick it in his twitching
mouth, but it fell on the floor again, good thing we didn't
have a carpet.

"No, I wouldn't advise it," I said. "You'd probably be
best off trying to forget about them. There's always a chance
that they'll forget about you."

Which is what happened. At least . . .

About three months after his tremulous dilemma, I ran
into him on National Avenue. He tried pretending not to
see me, but I wouldn't let him. We stopped in at the Slavia
Café, and he kept glancing around as if he were expecting
Sioux warriors to leap out at us from ambush. As soon as we
sat down, he lit up right away—that is, he tried to light up
right away, but he couldn't get match flame and cigarette to
meet. Finally, I lit it for him with my lighter.

"Thanks."

"Well?"

"Well, what?—You mean, THAT?"

"Yes, I mean THAT." The waiter brought him a glass of
wine, which Jarka immediately proceeded to pollute with
cigarette ashes. There were brown circles around his eyes,
maybe it was the nicotine starting to soak through. "You
told your wife, did you?"

"God, no!" It obviously set him back on his heels, he
scanned the café again as if through a revolving periscope.
His voice dropped to a hoarse whisper. He took a long drag

off his cigarette, and the falling ashes fouled his wine beyond potability. "They . . . like you said they would . . ."

"They forgot about you, right?" He was about to butt out his cigarette in the ashtray, but it fell in his lap instead. I didn't want to torture him anymore. He'd been through enough already. Better said: was going through enough. "You see?" I remarked, reassuringly, "I told you so. Everything's all right now, isn't it?"

He made a vain attempt to sip his tainted wine, gave it up, set the glass down, and spattered his necktie anyway. "Right," he said. I looked at my watch, and said that I had to go to an editorial meeting. I left him with his fireproof cigarettes, his polluted wine and his (obviously) gloomy thoughts.

But less than a year later, their power declined, with the arrival of the Prague Spring and Dubček, so it was all academic, or at least, they had other things to worry them for about a year. Jarka didn't wait that long. Even before the engines of the invading tanks had time to cool down, he and his wife had flown the coop, straight to Sweden. As far as I heard, he is still hammering away there enthusiastically, in that land of many hammers.

But to continue with the paradigmatic tale: for the first ten years the only signs of life were picture postcards, photographs which depicted, as I recall, a radiant image of his inner (interior) self: the narrow Asiatic face, the sad eyes. A farmer's overalls. Early in the second decade, letters began to arrive. With time, the handwriting grew increasingly craggy, as hard work took its toll on the lightness of his hand (which never was very light in the first place). A textile factory, a metal works, New Guinea oil fields, a few mines, and then a letter:

> *Well, Old Buddy, we are pushing fifty, you and me. It's getting harder to find work, they want younger guys for the better jobs. Nowadays I often have to work up to my waist in water . . . but it's good money.*
>
> *Your Old Buddy.*

Letters like the ones phonied up by *fizls* for Letters to the Editor of *Rudé Právo*, but these were undoubtedly genuine and truthful, no sentimentality, no sugary recollections like the ones in this text. No recollections at all, in fact. A slice of life. *"They want younger guys. . . ," "". . . up to my waist in water. . . ," "". . . it's good money."* A paradigm of the typical capitalist situation, which, it seems, is typical for those who don't know their way around. Přema, my Old Buddy, never knew his way around, anywhere.

The yearning (the paradigmatic one) was stronger in him than it is in me today. My sentimentality does not extend to physical homecomings. My returns are in my mind, or at best in the extravagance of words. I live for the future because there is nothing there waiting for me, because I know that there will never again be anything like the strawberry Marie, and even she is just a flimsy canvas, gossamer, not even a photograph, just a lightly sketched Japanese stylization, a pictograph of the beauty of green and gold forest years; in that, she is just like that entire land, like the hopeful sixties, I turn back to her and to them only in these doilies, hand-tatted out of ink instead of thread, homecomings like that can't bring disappointment, for in them there is none of the confrontation of model and image that is affected by time and *fizls*. Yes, Přema was more sentimental than I was, because no sonner had the *annus mirabilis*, the Spring of no Grace, begun, a missive arrived, his letters so craggy it was as if, up to his waist in water, he'd hit them with a sledgehammer.

Do you think, Old Buddy, that I could come home, now that you are having that revitalization of yours?

I consulted with a lady lawyer I had known since the days when you couldn't tell a defense attorney from a state prosecutor, but her, you could always tell. God knows how she survived. Because the law of our age of weary *fizls* is always to assume the worst, I could say it was in exchange for services that were withheld by my (old) buddy Jarka. Not that I believe it, but how else to explain it? The same kind of mystery as Jarka's *terror mulieris*. But I still don't believe it. Maybe she was the exception that occasionally (very rarely, I'd say) confirms the rule, a small irony, a small absurdity of the Age of the Great Terror. No, I just do not believe it. The lady lawyer was pretty, slender, but terribly energetic, with a terribly forceful lawyer's voice, and yet she got married, had three children, poor kids, they always looked like a military unit on guard duty, she was an awful mother, but a real dynamo, she set out to find the transcripts. I knew (it was in the newspapers back then) that in the trial with the grocer *et al*, Přema had been sentenced, in absentia, to two years.

She came back and said sharply in her bullhorn voice, "There are no transcripts."

"Are you certain? Isn't there a chance that they—"

"When I say there are no transcripts, then there are none. That's nothing out of the ordinary for the trials in the fifties. Somebody (understand?), simply needed (understand?), for them not to (understand?) exist. Your friend lucked out. From the legal point of view, it's perfectly safe. It will be—what, June? That's twenty years, anyway, and besides, there is no record of any sentence. Write him to come home, no fear."

Who was the one who wrote that, and then did himself in? Biebl? Young Neumann?[65] Ah, yes, *No Fear*. Not exactly the safest incantation. But the lady lawyer got up in her miniskirt and with her gait resembling that of a Soviet general, marched me to the door. A handshake with a pressure of some ten atmospheres. Poor little kids. "So long!" exceeding ten decibels.

"So come home, old buddy. You've learned to drive, you know English, I know some people at the British Embassy, I think you won't have any trouble getting a good job, and things here look fairly—if it lasts, of course . . ." (I wanted to see him, I wasn't being truthful, the desire to see him conquered truthfulness; I knew it wouldn't last. They say I'm pretending how smart I was, instead of admitting they were playing dumb. Everyone who knows the rules of the game even a little bit could have solved that simple equation.) I didn't write him not to come, that I didn't think it would last. I just wrote for him to wait until after the Party Congress in September.

I can't wait, Old Buddy, came his reply, *I've got my ticket
already. I sold everything, I'm coming by ship. Airplanes
cost too much. I'll be there end of summer.*
                                          Your Old Buddy.

Now for the second (or third, fourth, nth) paradigmatic
story. It was after the shit hit the fan. In Toronto, having betrayed the enemy, like others all over the western world, I
was padding myself a position on the beautiful corpse of
contemporary Czech literature, giving lectures at accom-
modating universities. Always the same crowd: a few professors of Slavic studies, one or two from Poli Sci, somebody
from the dean's office and the rest a bunch, no, rather a
swarm of lads and lasses, the kind I addressed at the philo-
sophical faculty of Charles University in Prague that black
January of 1969, when Jan Palach doused himself with his
holy gasoline (and one of them rose to ask, "Are you going
to write a new *Cowards* about it?" I laughed. "No. One of
you will have to do that." It was pompous, boastful, but I
meant it [I think] the way I said it. I didn't feel I had the
strength to describe the *annus mirabilis*, the Spring of no
Grace, the Spring of our hope[lessness]. Later, I tried anyway. Not intending to write another *Cowards*. Just a testa-
ment. A valediction. A balance sheet. An *Apologia pro vita
sua*. They responded—not the lads and lasses, but the ones
who were playing dumb—the way those who hadn't played
dumb during the Spring of no Grace, the ones who were as
smart as I was but in a different way, had reacted to *The
Cowards*. For me, what I expected to happen [it happened
just the way I expected, only a little sooner] was devastation,

for them it was salvation. For one of the ones who played
dumb, a car wreck on the highway to Utopia. Is he playing
dumb again? Or is it a tactical ploy by now? Does that mean
he is playing dumb again? Or does he believe it, the way I
believe he believed it when, in the years of the exhausted
executioners he rhapsodized about the munificent building
of socialism the way he declaimed for Ambassador Nichols,
"And the caterpillars slither aboard,"[66] accompanied by the
Disman Children's Chorus humming, "It's a long way to
Tipperary, it's a long way to go . . ."? And why not? Perhaps
he's right, in this absurd world of unlimited possibilities.
Perhaps it was just a car wreck on the highway to Utopia.
Nevertheless, from the vantage point of my life [our lives] it
was devastation all the same). I could tell from their eyes,
gazing at me with the solemnity of their solemn youth, with
profound eagerness, I could tell that although they'd "defected" they were still back there, that if anyone took the
annus mirabilis seriously, literally, they did (just as twenty
years before, those who believed in one thing and not in the
other did), and because they were eighteen, they weren't
playing dumb, they actually were dumb (like those twenty
years before them), but of course beautifully dumb, they
couldn't solve the simple equation, they didn't have the experience I (we) had, and they were here in body, but in
spirit they were back there, with the vague conviction that
"The fight must go on!" Soon, of course, they would forget
the chimera, the world would present them with other vil-
lainies, and because they were young, they assimilated much
more easily. Of course, they haven't forgotten. Perhaps—
but I won't indulge in prophesy. I think the ones at home

haven't forgotten either, but because they were young, they assimilated much more easily. Of course, they haven't forgotten. Perhaps—I won't indulge in prophesy, but beautiful wild music in the semibanned discotheques (where even Comrade bouncers bounce to the taut beat of that wild and wonderful music of unmistakable provenance: I've always believed in the indomitable defiance contained in that beautiful rhythmic music; barren themselves, they'll never annihilate it) continues to resound, with the beautiful Czech language of songs by a contemporary bard mocking the newspeak of their catechism.[67] I won't indulge in prophesy. In addition, there was always a number of couples dressed in European elegance (in this country, beards and long hair and jeans on university professors were all the rage), with bated breath, without so much as a yawn, they listened to me talk about books that they knew as well as I did (probably better, because, back home, I mostly read American novels). And after the lecture, after a few western questions (i.e., hopelessly naive, true innocents' questions) from attending professors, they would crowd around me, "Remember me? I talked with you when you were giving a talk in Rtyně"; ". . . when you were autographing books at Topič's"; ". . . at the book-signing at Mladá fronta." They handed me books to autograph that they had packed across the Atlantic Ocean like devotional relics, those most precious of my books, my sole true literary tributes, well-thumbed volumes lugged across the big pond in students' tote bags. I autographed them with the same signature I used to sign in Rtyně, at Topič's, as at Mladá fronta, they stood around for a long time, I couldn't remember any of them from back then, how could a person remember individual faces from crowded lecture halls, but as the only person on the podium, I remained supremely memorable. Reluctant to go out into the Canadian night, to Yonge and Bloor,[68] they finally had to, gradually they drifted outside. At the edge of the gradually shrinking crowd stood a couple dressed in very elegant European elegance, in fact, he wore a sky-blue bow tie, he was vaguely familiar, the tall blond fellow with eyes permanently downcast since he was a head taller than everyone else, and beside him, in a sealskin coat, Milena.

The sight of her brought swingtime Kostelec into Toronto's Sidney Smith lecture hall, the band dressed in blazers of the striped canvas ticking, the Port Arthur bar and bandleader Zetka, the blaring of six brasses that made the whole Port Arthur vibrate like a Disney cartoon and the thick honeyed tones of the saxes à la Lunceford flowing out of the windows of that bar, outside time and space. Always perched at the corner table, Milena with Lucie, Alena, with their glasses of wartime pop. Each of us (probably) has our own inaccessible earthly Garden of Eden, the fragrance of its cypresses wafts past us once, early in our lives, we pursue, we proceed, but we never quite attain it. My own Eden was this band, this music. My hearing was strangely affected, though: I listened, and heard the Platonic concept of beauty and happiness and the music of the spheres merge with the honeyed swing of the saxes. I could hear better than anyone else, certainly more profoundly than the others in the band. It was before we discovered Dixieland, before the United States entered the Great War, Mr. Maršík's shop still sold records with labels like Decca, Brunswick, Polydor. And

there must have been a hunger in me, the blues, more compelling than in all the fourteen band members, because on
one record with a Decca label I discovered Armstrong's "St.
James Infirmary Blues," his voice, his horn, Kid Ory's trombone, I lay awake half the night immersed in that sadly
beautiful bliss, but when I played the record the following
day in Benno's villa, the response was disappointing. They
were into swing, only brushed with the anguish of the blues,
for them, the supreme beauty of jazz was Fletcher Hender-
son, in full swing arrangement, the mildly pregnant sound of
a big band (Ah, for me too: the honeyed four-part harmony
of the saxes, the keen mute over the stream of honey, the
trombone in hat like a muffled bell over the honey of that
river—but second only to that came the blues, the blues of
my primal and private inadequacies, and the resultant yearning, Bechet's soprano sax, solitary, tight as a wire, wailing
unsentimentally among the strings of the guitar, dignified in
its despair, a classic.). "It's primitive," said Fonda, an incom-
parable virtuoso. "Ordinary three-part harmony, that's all,
it's simple." They shook their heads over it, and I, mortified,
stuck the record in my bag. And they cut loose with a great,
thundering, swinging swing Powerhouse, long (since) forgotten. So that I listened to jazz, but all I knew how to do
(a bit) was write, I spent exactly one day with that band,
I didn't pass muster, the rest of the war I spent with other,
obscure, ordinary little swing bands (Red Music, Betrieb-
skapelle Metallbauwerke, The Plhov Swingers), I played a
sorry tenor, Assembly of Swingers, Lock Up Today in My
Chest of Dreams, June in January, Cherokee, I was driven
out of Eden to the very fringes of Zetka's famous band.

Later on, of course, I wrote about it, wrote about the band
(those who can, do; those who cannot, write about it),[69]
that's why I'm going into this, although I've certainly written more than plenty about jazz: the best I've written (say,
the least bad stuff, or: the passable stuff, for people who hear
the way I do) was about jazz, but that's why I'm going into
it now, to explain why you won't find Milena in those writings. The reason is simple: it's a technical one. For those
who aspire to the extravagance of words, perhaps it is an en-
lightening one. But I mustn't and I don't want to be con-
ceited: at least it's a curiosity, of interest to a future historian
of the beginnings of Czech contemporary fiction: Hrabal,
Kundera, Vyskočil, Vostrá, Bělohradská, Beneš, Šotola, Salivarová, Klíma, Klimentiev, Prošková, Vaculík, Papoušek,
Kovtun, Vejvoda (I would add Páral, Fuks, but why did
they have to not hold out?), Körner, Pecka, Pujman, Pavel
(after all, they aren't friends of the enemy, they know the
Bible: *a time to keep silence and a time to speak*, they know that
in the enemy's domain, some things are simply not done:
like beating up on abstractivists, or standing at the graveside
of literature and glorifying the heroes of labor. Whodunits.
The past. Fairy tales. A triple path that can be trodden even
in the enemy's backyard. And then there is silence, the path
of heroes. Here it is impossible not to be melodramatic. Except of course maybe it's all just a farce. The chronological
juxtaposition of Palach and our miserable careers, of the
strawberry Marie and Auschwitz, that's how it has always
been, no fear. And don't despair. Anton Pavlovich Chekhov
wrote: *"Be joyful, cultivate a less complex notion of life, because in
reality, life is much simpler. And it remains moot to ask if life, about*

which we know nothing, deserves all the agonizing reflections that so exhaust our Russian intellect." But in the light of the negligible volume of my own personal experiences, I still think that Chekhov was talking through his hat when he spoke of simplicity, unless of course he meant the simplicity of the three cardinal conditions: Birth, Procreation, Demise, the three ultimate elements of our hopelessness.); marginal information for a footnote: "THE COWARDS, *a novel by a young author, who is significant primarily in a historical context: after years of socialist realism and novels influenced by socialist realism (Ptáčník, Očenášek) he was the first to bring to Czech prose a first-hand, deliberately subjective perception of life, an unfettered treatment of motifs that until then had remained taboo (eroticism, jazz), and a colloquial narrative with slang in the dialogue."* But I mustn't be overly modest, either; that, as the Holy Church teaches us, would be hypocrisy too. I truly believe that this novel will survive me in Czech literature. (Of course, *Evening Songs* survived Hálek,[70] but who actually reads them? I mean, for the pleasure of it, not because he has to, the way a child reads his primer. But perhaps—I hope—*The Cowards* will remain, as did *Tales from the Lesser Quarter*—It's probably not a pretense, maybe it is conceit. People do go back and reread *Tales from the Lesser Quarter* now and then.[71] And maybe it's not conceit. I have yet to work my way through to the stoicism of the sages, the only wise view *sub specie aeternatis.* One thing is certain, to avoid being totally expendable, every human being must produce something useful in the course of a lifetime: a pair of shoes, an appendectomy, a child, a well-kept set of accounts, a novel, a plowed field, the winning goal, a good deed for the sick, a

machine part, a good dinner, thousands of other things like
that, and from the perspective of light years, Shakespeare's
immortality is indistinguishable from the immortality of that
pair of shoes.) So I think (I hope) that when I go the way
of all flesh, *The Cowards* will outlive me the way my father's
orthopedic shoes outlived master cobbler Zahálka of Kostelec; that there will be some people (maybe young people)
who will be entertained by the story of Danny, Irena,
Benno and the other girls and guys around the band in Kostelec. I console myself with the thought that I did the best I
could, and that I never wrote anything just to appeal to anyone but myself (not counting articles, epilogues—and even
those weren't written to appeal to anyone but rather to
shield things that didn't appeal to those in power). I truly
think that, from the author's point of view, the decisive cri-
terion of literature is his own conscience. Of course, the
determining factor in the history of literature will be the
question, *"It comes from the bottom of my heart / But is it Art?"*
(The author of these lines is the contemporary Czech writer
Milena McGraw, one of my beautiful Czech girls from the
sixties, the age of disconcerted *fizls*, who married wisely
[which doesn't mean it wasn't for love] a man from Hixson,
Tennessee; like me, she was a hard-core Anglophile and
there she sits in Tennessee and writes contemporary Czech
literature and smuggles it into the domain of overworked
fizls.) That equation, of course, is also simple: If it is to be
Art, it must be *from the bottom of* one's *heart*. The compleat
cliché. The trouble is that not everything that comes *from the
bottom of* one's *heart* is *Art*. Still, I think that if literary criticism is not to be a hated vocation, if it is not to be almost as

inhuman as what the Kolder report writes (over dear Saša's signature), it should be as precise (no, even more precise, though I probably think that just because I'm a Christian, in the sense of the commandment "Do unto others . . .") in discerning *Art* as it is in discerning traces of *heart's bottom*, and in destroying whatever shows no trace of heart's bottom. Forgive me—I can't help it—just as I hate *fizls* and snoot-punchers and torturers, I hate the critic who presents our bloody failures as crimes, as the contemptible products of our conceit, of our hunger for glory; who derides our bitter defeats (consider Khrushchev, who, like the thief on the right will, I believe, find salvation; read the second volume of his memoirs and recall the life that, Anton Pavlovich's blatherings to the contrary, was complex rather than simple; you don't kick a man when he's down. Remember Dudintsev?[72] After a flawed book, he was down. The only thing worthy of contempt is dishonesty, writing to appeal to someone other than oneself. Failing artistically is not. We all produce flawed works. Faulkner knew something about that, after all, and we differ only in the measure of our failures, the relative barrenness of the islands that are our books.)

A few curiosities about the Czech novel called *The Cowards*. There is some Dixieland in it (the Bob Crosby kind, that is, with the tenor added onto the New Orleans front line). Historically, it rings true: there really was a Bob Crosby kind of Dixieland in Zetka's band toward the end of the war; of course, they played from the sheet music of Jack Bulterman's arrangement of "Liza Likes Nobody," imported from Amsterdam; how it was imported, I've described in *The Bass Saxophone*. But that was only now and

then, we didn't actually cotton onto the concept of Dixieland until the end of the war (in Rychnov nad Kněžnou,
they had real live Dixie then, with Jirka Šlitr[73] at the piano).
Mostly at the Port Arthur it was big band: six brasses, four
(late in the war sometimes even five) saxophones, plus the
rhythm section. But try putting fifteen or sixteen functional
characters in a novel. They simply don't fit. So I abbreviated
the band. Even so, I practically lost drummer Brynych,
Venca Štern on the trombone, and bass man Jindra Kašpar.
They are only there in references. But the front line is there
(almost) in its entirety: Benno, Lexa, Danny, and the piano
(Fonda) and the guitar (Harýk). Each of them plays his own
compelling solo part, and each of them plays in the ensemble choruses. Zetka, the bandleader isn't there; Dixieland
doesn't have a leader, and that's why Milena isn't there
either. Nor is Vláďa Nosek and Vláďa Celba, because they
played altos, and Pepíček Syrovátko and Jirka Ptáček, second and third trumpets. And Mirek Chmelař and the
younger Syrovátko, second and third trombones. Even the
third Syrovátko on the baritone. I just couldn't squeeze them
in. In other words, I'm saying that Benno is Pavel Bayerle,
Lexa is Vladimír Stejskal, Fonda is Vladimír Šilhánek, Harýk
is Jarýk Celba, and also, God help me, that Irena is Járinka
Fibírová, Rosťa is Bouša Španiel, Dagmar (In *The Swell Season*, I made Dagmar into Marie: the radiant pool in the
Rembrandt frame is much too intense, the name Marie
balked at wearing the mask, which for that matter is unnecessary by now anyway.) Dresslerová is Marie Dyntarová,
Lucie is Hannie Hartmanová, and so forth. And that Danny
is me. That, of course, is only half true. I could quote Goethe

again, that everything in literature is *Wahrheit und Dichtung;* a blend of the two. But I would rather quote Benno, that is, Pavel Bayerle, who was fat and good-natured, and because he was half Jewish, he spent his adolescence in Jewish terror (including a time toward the end of the war in the concentration camp for *Halbjuden und arische Gatten von Juden;* that too is accurate in *The Cowards*: he did come home from this concentration camp before the end of the war and by war's end was playing at the Port Arthur again) and stayed fat and good-natured until his splendid death (it couldn't have been more splendid, after all: he died during a concert his band was giving—he became a professional jazz band leader— in the middle of a tune right there onstage, dead on the spot of a heart attack); in the autumn after the troops marched in, he pulled himself together and came to see me in the apartment with the lovely basilica outside the window, looking for some sort of text from me, a manifesto for him to read on tour—another manifesto: Manifesto Opposing the Occupation. But he soon got scared. His band was perhaps the first one of all that played for the Soviet army. But how could I hold it against him, good old Benno, who had barely survived one protectorate and who in fact paid for it with his premature death, forty-seven years young. And when the bomb called *The Cowards* blew up, late in the age of exhausted executioners when the mighty arm of the Party was purging bothersome ones (pioneers of the liberalization: Fikar, Grossman, Hiršál, Lederer),[74] and their hack writers gave the signal for naive attribution (in their case, not naive but deliberate) identifying me totally with Danny, and, ignoring everything that didn't fit, drawing Danny as

the ultimate in bourgeois baseness and cynicism (the more
zealous of them even unearthed in him antisemitism,
Titoism and fascism, with the kind of superficiality Patty
Hearst applied when she called comfortable—compared to
the Gulag Archipelago—American prisons concentration
camps and labeled the country where you can relieve yourself with impunity into a chamber pot in the shape of the
president, a country where unqualified freedom is not even
qualified by consideration of one's neighbor, she labeled that
country as fascist), at that point the scared Benno logically
assumed that if the Party had ordered the identification of
the main hero, who actually behaves and speaks relatively
decently in the novel, some eager beavers at a regional level
would surely identify other characters, on and on, drawing
logical conclusions for those so identified, who not only are
cynical, but use foul language, condemned as nonexistent by
Stalin himself (*On Marxism in Linguistics*). And because there
were already copies of the novel circulating in his native
Kostelec naming names in pencil in the margins (Mr.
Moutelík, a perfectly decent class enemy himself, told
Rosťa, "Someday, they're going to build him a monument
in Kostelec for that novel. And do you know what it'll be?"
Rosťa shook his head, the class enemy declared augustly, "A
sandstone phallus!"), the frightened Benno decided to try to
save himself. He wrote a letter to *Literární noviny* and in it,
with an amalgam of fear and courage, because he was a
buddy, he also tried to defend me. "Everything in the novel
is true," he wrote, adding that he could testify to it (it would
have been genuinely false witness), with one sole exception:
he, Benno, never used dirty words, especially in the context

of things that everyone holds holy (he was using the words of the critics: Běhounek, Rybák, Jan Nový) because he, Benno, is and always has been a patriot. Apologetics aside, though, the fact is that the original author of most of the cynical pronouncements around things holy was not Benno, but Vráťa Blažek; we ran into each other on Wenceslas Square, both of us in deep shit (he had just been turfed out of Barrandov Studios for his script for the ostensibly Tito-istic film *The Third Wish*), and Vráťa said, "You really pissed me off, Pepi. I was the one who came up with all the dirty sayings in that novel of yours. And I'm not even in the book!" Well, he wasn't. I had more than enough heroes (i.e., characters who play a substantive part in a novel) without him. As with the alto players and the second and third trumpets and trombones, there was no room in *The Cowards* even for Vratislav Blažek,[75] the *spiritus agens* of the fireworks of human *(nihil humani a me)* levity that is the cynicism of hard times, did not have room in *The Cowards*. Unfortu-nately. If Vráťa was a genius at anything, it was the epigram, the bon mot, the remark that exposed—in the words of today—a false consciousness (and of course, he was a genius at song lyrics, precursor to Suchý. *"They two were true love going steady, and only seventeen years old, and people said they weren't ready, and people called them rude and bold"*—the ten-derest of Czech pop songs, and incidentally the best descrip-tion of the heroes and the heroines of the novel in question that didn't have room for Vráťa). Let it be said here, if nowhere else.

So that identifying characters with people is always flawed, although the history of modern literature is riddled with it (so for that matter is the history of older literature, but there it no longer matters who modeled for the characters, they've long since been forgotten), and it isn't any specialty of mine or of Czech literature. True, others were more circumspect (How long did it take for Lieutenant Dub to be recognized as an eminent professor of the Czech language?),[76] while yet others were more foolhardy (go look in the New Jewish Cemetery in Prague, the resting place of Franz Kafka; there, on a huge tombstone you will find Mr. Načeradec, businessman in ready-to-wear, *und seine getreue Gattin*, and his faithful wife Irma; you don't have to be from Rychnov nad Kněžnou to—Oh, the stories. That's how I first encountered such identifications in Czech literature, long before I read that Robert Cohn in Hemingway was in fact Harold Loeb, and that the insatiable young lady in Lawrence's *Women in Love* was Katherine Mansfield, warts and all: once during the war, I had to go to a village the other side of Rychnov for some honey, and in the cottage kitchen there was a tableau on the wall, from imperial Austria, students in high stiff collars, and the professor with the highest collar of all, and a mighty mustache. Like anyone, I'm always drawn to the camp of old photographs. I stepped closer for a better look, and something struck me.

I turned to the granny: "Tell me, isn't the professor here the same one that Poláček wrote about riding his bicycle, the one who—what was his name—?"

"Which Poláček?" the old woman snapped at me suspiciously—I didn't understand.

"The one who wrote the novels, the one who used to live near—"

"Oh, THAT Poláček! That stinking Jew," grumbled the old woman antisemitically, war or no war, "the one who bad-mouthed all of our gentry here!" I didn't dare ask any more, the old woman was still grumbling under her breath as she tied up the parchment on the jar of honey—and so you really don't have to be from Rychnov nad Kněžnou to stand over the grave of Irma Načeradec and contemplate the foolhardiness of the unfortunate Mr. Poláček.). People get upset, and yet I was naive enough to think (as, I believe, did Poláček) that what my novel radiates is love. That it is a veritable declaration of love (in fact, an explicit one, another key phrase) to all my buddies, to all my loves from those youthful years of mine. Of course, I underestimated the human capacity for malice. And that was why Irena got so upset with me that to this day she won't speak to me, even though it actually isn't her, because what do I know about her beyond that thin facade of her beauty, although (as her husband was supposed to have told her: "What's your problem? He describes you as being untouchable. Were you really like that? It's not how I remember you!") the only thing I wrote about her that was true was that she didn't want me and (almost) never let me near her, although that one kiss is a historical fact, but even the surviving reverend fathers couldn't consider that immoral; and I did give her beautiful, long, slender legs in the novel, whereas in fact her legs were more like hockey sticks. Everything is an amalgam of *Dichtung und Wahrheit*, and of course Dagmar never did anything naughty with Herbert Percy Siddell, she was much too well brought up for that, too devout, while the writer is a creature possessed by demons; when I was writing it, though, it never occurred to me that anyone would be identified; when I was writing it, it never even occurred to me that it would ever get published; but when I was taking it to the printer's, it may have crossed my mind. Except that a writer is a creature pursued by demons, he would even kill his own mother, as Faulkner said truthfully, so he could finish writing a book. I'm genuinely sorry, to think of human deceitfulness, and Kostelec, and the gossip there about the devout girl in the little blue coat (it was a different girl, but I couldn't keep expanding the number of main roles, so I attributed the unseemly behavior to Marie). And yet, she forgave me, she is a Christian. I apologize, strawberry Marie, for everything I did that offended you, I admire you. I always remain true to my old loves, because they were all platonic.

And *habent sua fata libelli. Et critici.* I don't have to write about that, there are records. There were public apologies to me, recantations, the Party passed a Resolution to Authorize to undo the earlier Resolution to Prohibit, and the novel was published again (changes: yes, I did change *Russkies* to *soldiers* in a few places, I blue-penciled—at least, I think I did, I don't have a copy of the first edition on hand—some parts about the massacre of SS-men, all in response to polite requests by Karel Kostroun who, having been infiltrated into the Stalinist anthill that was the Central Committee of the Party, led the battle for the ludicrous re-habilitation of this one Czech novel. That's how things were done in those days, and again: a blue pencil is not specific to the dictatorship of the proletariat. Faulkner applied it, in fact at the request of H. L. Mencken, everybody has done it, everywhere, the kind of blue-penciling that doesn't alter the substance of the work. In fact, I even added a few episodes, at no one's behest, or even suggestion, for example the one about Mr. Řimbálník berating the SS-Scharführer in the sweetshop, and also, I think, the one about Harýk's act of heroism at the anti-Jewish art exhibit, a few episodes that underscore the substance of the book.). Which brings me to the question that everybody always asks me. Why *The Cowards*? And who are the cowards? Cross my heart and hope to die, I don't know. I don't know why and I don't know who. It just occurred to me, that's all. Maybe it's a challenge to take a look at the truthfulness of the bathos of lofty words (like the word *cowards*). It may have been, in fact it surely was, ridiculous to practice saluting and "About Face!" with sticks on our shoulders instead of rifles against the backdrop of the distant rumble of the approaching cannonade! But as Professor Černý[77] once said: "And what do you think they should have done with you there in brewery courtyard?" Yes, really, what should they? In an army, there has to be discipline, that's a truism that applies. So, unfortunately, I truly don't know why or who.

The recanting, the apologies even appeared in the press. But maybe I have two stories that didn't. One is the truth, I don't know about the second; maybe it's part of the modern folklore of a nation renowned for the mass production of anecdotes. It is not an improbable story, though.

The first: I was in the hospital, the miserable hepatitis sanatorium in Motol, no radio, no television, their library consisted of wall-to-wall Czech socialist realism (that is how I became more or less of an expert in the field), friends sent me detective mysteries (because as soon as a book is inside the walls of an infectious hepatitis ward, it has to stay there, and detective mysteries are not that important. Though actually, they are. In life situations like that, they're more precious than Shakespeare. So I became more or less of an expert on detective stories, too), the fear of dying weighed heavily on me (I'd been married less than two years, I was in love with my young wife, those days I didn't have the slightest desire to die), I was despondent. There was a young woman doctor there, rather pretty, who kept hovering around my bed, and not just during rounds. She made me nervous; I saw it as an indication that I was a candidate for death, otherwise why would she show such an interest in me? Finally—she actually blushed as she spoke—she said, "Do you still remember when they denounced you on the radio a while back?" I certainly remembered, but I didn't recall who it had been. It was a trio: a poet (later I found out that he was Ivo Štuka; later still, he became a great pal to me; now, I think he has become normalized again), a laborer and an officer.

"Well," said the doctor, "the officer was my late husband. Don't be angry with him. He was miserable about it afterwards." I hastened to reassure the pretty, tearful doctor that I had never been angry (I spoke the truth. It isn't in my nature to be angry at people. Must be some strange kind of psychopathology. Certainly not a virtue.). "You see, he hadn't read your novel at the time. He was an officer, he was on the editorial staff of *Czechoslovak Soldier* magazine and that night he was on call. They called from headquarters and ordered him to order an officer to go to the radio building.

He asked if a regular army sergeant would do, and they said no, the order called for an officer. So he had to go himself. They stuck a ready-made script in his hand as soon as he got there, and he barely had time to skim it before they were on the air, live. He didn't know your book, but he had to read what they had written for him, you understand, you're a guy, you've been in the army yourself. It was an order, and he was an officer. But he knew right off he had done something wrong. He got hold of a copy of *The Cowards* as soon as he could, and read it, and believe me, he genuinely enjoyed it, but that made it all the worse for him. He wanted to write you and apologize but he never knew how, he kept putting it off, and then he had to fly to the Soviet Union, on army business. There they were supposed to fly Odessa-Moscow, a storm grounded the flight, but some military plane was taking off and it took them because they were officers. And that plane crashed and my husband was killed." The doctor, only recently widowed (I heard her confession in the spring of '60, the campaign around *The Cowards* had been in the spring of 1959), burst into tears, I was ill at ease because I had actually never been angry at anybody, but how to make her believe me.

That's how it was done back then, in the age of recovering executioners and petty *fizls* about to be disconcerted. The second story? You know the Awards to Top Employees? Toward the end of the year, the official in charge of culture goes to the local Books, National Enterprise store, and buys the requisite number of books. It always seemed to me that this was where the manager got rid of books that didn't sell. Anyway, at the Radlice Dairies, the clerk in charge of culture set out on that very errand, and it so happens that the bookstore had just received a shipment of another book that wouldn't sell. Or so it seemed to the manager, on the basis of the jacket text (which reminds me, just a mini-story here: as a first-time published author I was hanging around a bookshop where *The Cowards* was out on display on the counter, and I saw a gentleman. He was flipping pages of the books on the counter, reading dust covers. He picked up a book with a title something like *Night of Swastikas*, he read the front flap of the dust cover, he hesitated, he put *Night of Swastikas* back down on the counter and—picked up *The Cowards*! He started reading the front flap. From it, he learned that he held in his hand a satirical novel which un-equivocally exposes the quintessence of the bourgeoisie, and presents a penetrating critique of the conduct of the bour-geoisie during the May Revolution. The gentleman did not look like a proletarian, he snapped the book shut without finishing the dust jacket, probably no great fan of socialist realism either, tossed it on the counter, reached deliberately for *Night of Swastikas* and strode off to the cashier. I cringed with the pain of a wounded author.). The manager of the bookshop in Radlice must also have judged the book by its dust cover text, and he sold the official in charge of culture for the Radlice Dairies twelve volumes for twelve top apos-tles of socialist labor. Back at the Dairies, each was duly stamped with the stamp of the Revolutionary Trades Union Movement, inscribed by hand with a dedication like: "To the top milk clarifier operator" and so forth, and distributed at a small gathering under the Red Banner of Radlice Dairies, Holder of the Red Banner. Soon afterwards, the trouble started and the petty *fizls*, with a (momentary) surge of self-confidence, set out in pairs to various Books, National Enterprise stores to confiscate unsold copies. They didn't find a lot to confiscate, right after the first attack was published (in the newspaper *Práce*) store managers had pricked up their ears, and *The Cowards* vanished under the counter, saved for steady customers, in the meantime paid for out of the managers' own pockets, leaving nothing for the poor little *fizls*. Except the manager of the store in Radlice, in an effort to add credibility to his contention that the book had sold out so quickly, admitted that twelve of the sold copies (the only ones legitimately sold—the rest sat hidden under the counter) had been bought by the Dairies as annual awards. Off to the Dairies went the *fizls*, to interrogate the twelve top employees, all of them dimwits who had lost the book! Or else they were addled, they'd lent the book to somebody and already forgotten who! Every single one! Dimwittedness to a degree that was mathematically totally improbable, yet totally explicable.

So that's how things were done. Let these stories stand as *pars pro toto* of the kind of folklore around what could be called the transgression of my youth. But back to Milena. An inconspicuous, pleasant looking girl from Opočno, her daddy an old-school schoolteacher. She spoke (still speaks) with a clear trace of an Eastern Bohemian pronunciation and intonation, a great buddy of mine. We were students of English at Charles University together, we crammed for exams together, once or maybe twice there was a faint sign of intimacy between us, but only within the norms of lovely Kostelec; a touch of a leg under a table, hands squeezed during a lecture. A young person experiences (experienced) dozens of such transient encounters, nothing came of them and what remained was the friendship, and as I moved away from Kostelec, in time and in space, Milena remained a tiny stone in the mosaic of my native town, in the memory of an age when a *fizl*, an informer, a stool pigeon was beneath a hired killer; a human louse, lower than a louse: no Kostelec girl would ever have married an informer, even if she loved him. They were all great patriots. That's what Milena was like, a jolly girl, with a Slavic face, a country manner of speaking, words sweetly abbreviated with vowels folding neatly into consonants.

And there she stood before me (practically), unchanged, dressed in European elegance, her husband with a bow tie and a nasal voice, "My name is Pavlas. You probably don't remember me any more, but I took Milena to one of your talks at the National Hall in Smíchov. Pepík . . . what you said about literature, you know, you said it so beautifully." His voice turned mushy (I never really understood what *mushy* meant, until he said how BEAUTIFULLY I had said it), and his eyes filled with tears. The expression "The Sentimental Fool" surfaced in my mind—derived I think from Al Jolson's film *The Singing Fool*—and later on, among my wife and I and a few friends, the name stuck, although like most nicknames, it got abbreviated to: The Fool.

The Fool wiped his eye with a finger with a ring on it, and insisted that we HAD to come visit. So we did. They lived in a nice part of Toronto, near Lake Ontario, my wife never wanted to go but I went because of my buddy Milena. Nothing about the apartment struck me. Except maybe the fact that, contrary to old Czech socialist traditions, they were not very generous with alcohol, all there was to drink was a weak aperitif out of a $2.50 mickey. The Fool talked and was mushy. The Prague Castle, Hradčany, and would he ever see it all again, Hradčany. And the cottage . . . his cottage, he passed around pictures of the cottage they had left behind, fully furnished, complete with a gas refrigerator. Being a woman, my wife noticed that the Toronto apartment was far from being fully furnished. "See, they're planning to go back," said my wife. "Everything they have is collapsible, portable, packable. And they haven't got a carpet. A show-off like The Fool, and no carpet?"

The Fool proved to be a compulsive, arrogant friend, pushy and reproachful. Every week he would phone and say: "Why don't you phone me, Pepík? What kind of a friend are you? You really must come over!" He was equally aggressive in demanding introductions to people, especially the ones who "mean something," and I knew them all, because I'm one of them too (but what does that mean I mean, then?). Over time, I introduced him to Karel Ančerl, who was director of the Toronto Philharmonic, to Jaroslava Blažková, a writer who meant something, to Eva Límanová, Ivan Passer's[78] sister, who was married to a professor, and when Ivan came to Toronto, I introduced him to Ivan too, and he promised to drop by when he was in New York, and to painter Ladislav Guderna, everybody. The Fool moved from party to party, wearing different colored bow ties, and custom-made suits in light grey, beige and neon, and, in his nasal voice, toadied his way up everybody's backside. With Milena always by his side (toadying to no one), we would chat about old times, gossip about shades of Kostelec, her voice retaining its intonation like someone out of J. Š. Kubín. Now and then The Fool would get really offended that we didn't phone, he'd sulk, but he'd soon come around. At home he was a petty tyrant, the apartment had to be shipshape, Milena confided in my wife that when he gets up in the morning, he has to have his slippers in exactly the right place so that he could just swing his feet out of bed without even looking, and if his feet didn't swing right into the precisely placed slippers, "there's hell to pay!" Milena told my wife.

The Fool was an old Party member (since 1945) and an architect by profession. That didn't mean anything, there are always plenty of Party members in various stages of fidelity, disillusionment, estrangement, crisis or conscience pangs. The Fool was no different from the rest, except maybe when the conversation shifted to the U.S.S.R., he brought everything back to the common denominator of Hradčany Castle, and a moist and mushy "What if I never see it again?" "You just wait, they'll go back!" said my wife. "Everything they have is collapsible. And have you ever seen such homesickness?"

At about the same time, a letter arrived:

Old Buddy,

It probably wasn't meant for us to be in the same place at the same time. Greetings from Kostelec. Surprised, are you? But once I was in Europe, I said to myself, Oh well, what's the worst that can happen. I am home, I got a job right off, at the foundry in Hronov.

"A fine mess," I thought to myself, as Vixi used to say.[79] A classic Czech story. A game of musical continents. The only thing missing is for me to be in Australia instead of in Canada.

Old Buddy,
You don't know what it's like, after twenty years, to hear them talking Czech on TV.

I replied.

Old Buddy,
I do understand. When you get over it, and if you still understand Czech, listen to what they're saying on the TV in Czech, and check to see if it is truly Czech.

But a very fat worm of doubt was burrowing inside me. It was born of signals from old letters that were smashed with a sledgehammer.

"They want younger guys for the better jobs . . . work up to my waist in water . . . to Melbourne, maybe there's better jobs to be had there . . . you know how it is, Old Buddy, the worker always gets stepped on . . . meanwhile there's enough work . . . they say next year there won't be."

Authentic fragments of reality and not what distinguishes socialist realist fiction. I was afraid. Afraid that future letters, Old Buddy, would not be about hogs and excursions with the UAC to the GDR for IWD.[80] Afraid that my Old Buddy (true, he had once betrayed the enemy, and he had even been outfitted with an illegal transmitter and the pistol that he showed me in the passageway), who hadn't been in the country when the executioners were being run ragged, who never believed much in the extravagance of words and so censorship is a meaningless concept to him, afraid that this Australian proletarian might fall for the rhetoric of the workers' paradise, with no unemployment, where work (unskilled labor) is well-paid, where the death of literature and offended emigrants' mothers rest on the foundation of laborers' pensions, benefits that rest on the foundation of vertical graves, the uranium mill and arrests for one and all. I was afraid because I didn't want my Old Buddy to harden, to turn against me because I had betrayed the enemy, who was transformed into an ally by the passage of time and a different authentic society. Because heaven knows what his values are, a drudge who wasn't there then, probably the same as other drudges who never were there (but what do I know about them? Does freedom, in the oldest, still unsullied, sense of the word, really mean no more to them than my buddy Lojza's fat hog? Even Lojza, a writer too, could tell the difference between enemy and ally: even Lojza saw fit to stand up for my Leona. What do I know about common sense, which may be closer to the most profound truths than the Science of sciences and the teaching of all teachings of all teachings?),[81] a drudge who succumbed to a nostalgia even fiercer than that of The Fool, steadfast even in the face of tanks and reports of doom. I was afraid that they might inoculate him with their devastating oversimplification of reality: that anyone who fails to agree, down to the last broken iota under the last superfluous exclamation point, has betrayed the enemy, is a murderer of murderers, an enemy of amiable enemies. But for a long time, I received no more letters.

In the meantime, The Fool kept inviting us over, calling, sulking, showing up at get-togethers, Czech and Canadian alike (he got a job at City Hall, he was an urban planner, and he worked on the reconstruction of China-town), his salmon-colored bow tie showed up at parties thrown by the Mayor, and City Councilors, candidates for municipal office, within a year and a half, he knew them all personally: the Liberals and the Progressive Conservatives, the New Democrats, the Creditists, the only ones he avoided were the Communists, but there weren't a lot of those. And all the while, incessantly, Hradčany . . . Petřín Hill . . . tree-lined Stromovka . . . and my cottage! My cottage and my cottage.

Another summer arrived—The Fool and Milena and their son (they had a son, a rangy kid who had just graduated high school and had been accepted at the School of Archi-tecture in Toronto) had spent the previous summer in Florida with the Zemáneks, I had introduced them. A for-mer United Nations employee who had defected. The Fool raved about how close they'd become over the summer. The year before they went to the Maritimes; lots of new friendships there too, plenty of new Czech friends, and it's so lovely there. . . . This year, finally, to Europe. Greece, Italy, France. They sent their precious Renault overseas by freighter, the same car they had shipped over from Prague on a different freighter three years earlier.

And summer went. Summers are always short, they get shorter as what's left of life gets shorter. September, and then October. Something was missing. Couldn't tell what. Then I realized: The Fool's phone calls. The call of nostalgia, the greenwood beneath Hradčany Castle. . . . For the first time in my life I dialed The Fool's number. "The number you are calling is not in service. Please check the number and try your call again." Something almost resembling sorrow. It was the first week in October, Indian summer in the land of the Indians. After all, they must be back already, Milena had a job teaching high school French, the school year had begun a while back in September.

I called City Hall.

"Mr. Karel Pavlas is no longer with us."

"Where—?"

"I've no idea. 'Bye."

I hung up. What happened?

"They went back," said my wife. "I told you they would. Everything they had was portable."

"What if they drowned?" I said. A strange sorrow (why strange? Milena was a buddy.) permeated my mind. "Do you remember? The ferry between Greece and Italy? The one that sank in August and drowned a thousand passengers?"

"No, we'd have heard," said my wife. "Oh, no. They packed up everything packable, they collapsed everything collapsible, and carried off everything portable. Even the car, didn't you register that? No, they're in Prague. And they're filing their report on us, in the shadow of Hradčany."

Indeed: our friends concluded that that was the most probable of all possible alternatives. They eliminated the one about the ferry. And that was where it stayed, soon nothing was left of The Fool but a comical memory.

November arrived, and two weeks of it passed. Somebody knocked at the door. I opened it. The same way I had understood the true meaning of the word *mushy* the first time I met The Fool, this time I understood how a person can really age ten years in three months. There in the doorway stood Milena, ten years older: brown hair turned gray, green eyes ringed in gray-black frames by Rembrandt, a network of wrinkles, weary as a little lost pup.

"Milena, what's wrong? What happened?"

"Oh," she said. "Karel went back." And she burst into tears.

She wept, we kept refilling her glass with the whiskey she used to only sip symbolically, she got tipsy, and talkative. Once they were in Europe, they couldn't resist making a small side trip from Greece to Yugoslavia. No matter what a person does, that corner of the world, *fizls* and all, draws us, at least to get a glimpse. From there, it was Austria, The Fool decided they should at least set eyes on a bit of the Native Land. Yes, I can almost hear The Fool saying it, with a capital N and a capital L. No, he probably said Native Soil. They drove right up to the border and stared (across a bare strip of Native Soil enhanced with buried personnel mines, festooned with barbed wire, inhabited by a flock of border guards accompanied by dogs, wolf and shepherd mix, the firmest bite in the world, better than a bulldog's) at the Native Soil, which reached out and grabbed The Fool by his heartstrings, "Milena," quoth he, "I Shall Return Home." A beautiful little scene, straight out of the Party propaganda press, even the misuse of Halas,[82] everything right and proper.

"And the kid too," Milena added, through her tears. "Said he wants to go for beers with his buddies," she said, drawing out her vowels in the classical Eastern Bohemian accent. "Said he missed that in Toronto, and besides, home is home." She broke into sobs.

"But Milena," I interrupted her weeping, "your permits had expired, you were outside the country illegally by then, weren't you?"

"And how come you're here?" my wife asked, simultaneously, a duet of questions. "Did you break up?"

Milena blushed. "That's what they think in school," she said. "I told them that he took a six-month contract job in France, but they don't believe me. They think he dumped me."

My wife: "And didn't he?"

"And didn't they arrest the two of them, being abroad without valid travel permits?" I made it a duet again.

"No, he really didn't dump me," said Milena. "And we had permits," she blushed (because in those days, nobody got permits to travel, and if somebody had one, he probably wasn't a nobody), "until the end of August. We never told anybody. And Karel and the boy went back the last day of August."

"And what about you? Are you here on an expired permit, or an extended one?" my wife asked mercilessly.

More tears. "That's right," she wailed, "an expired one. Karel is trying to get it extended for another year, I have a contract here for the next school year—"

"And that's why you didn't go back with them?" asked my heartless wife. "Baloney!"

It hit me. I glanced at my old friend. Black semicircles, hair that in summer had still been a beautiful dark brown now streaked with a witch's silver, high cheeks now drooping into jowls, fans of wrinkles. It hit me. Things came together, connected. That aggressive friendship, making contacts, the parties, Czech ones, municipal ones. That mushy brown-nosing of everyone important. The interest in the politics of a land that has never seen dictatorship, politics that seem boring to old cossacks like us. And the girl sitting over a green soda pop at the Port Arthur. The old thought resurfaced from back then . . . that no decent girl from Kostelec would ever have married an informer . . . even if she loved him. . . . And in Austria, a glimpse of the Native Soil, when she finally realized that for twenty years she'd been living with a *fizl*. Hence the abrupt aging. And that was why she was here alone, even (though that somehow doesn't figure, somehow a lot) without her son, a girl from the mosaic of Kostelec where a *fizl* was less than a louse—

She hesitated before answering, I watched her, waiting.

Milena said, "He . . . sent me back here . . . to save our stuff . . . we left it . . . behind . . ."

Ah, that was it. The custom-made suits. What wasn't quite as portable, packable. Aha.

"But please, don't tell anyone that I'm here. I just couldn't stand being by myself one more day."

We didn't. But Toronto is a village, like every expatriate Prague is. While I was as silent as the grave, and so (says she) was my wife, Milena ran into an old pupil of hers from the Dejvice Economic School one day on Yonge Street, Toronto's Wenceslas Square. And the word was out.

So the secret became public knowledge and was perceived as a psychological riddle. We went at it a number of ways, with Eva and with Hanka and with my wife. It remained unclear, at least one aspect of it did.

What did seem clear was that Karel was a *fizl*. The women maintained that they had known that from the outset. The portable stuff. The instant friendships, and so forth. "Yes, but," I broke into the women's logic, "if he was a *fizl*, then they went back to Europe already decided to go back. Evidence of that might be that they had their car shipped to Europe, which doesn't make financial sense, you can rent a car in Europe cheap, certainly cheaper than shipping it twice, there and back. So they obviously weren't counting on shipping it back. So far so good." And that strange (why strange?) sorrow filled my soul. "But why would they leave stuff that was collapsible, packable, portable in Toronto? It figures that they gave up their flat. But putting their stuff in storage doesn't figure. And why, pray tell, would a *fizl*, returning to his home base, to *fizl* headquarters, whey would he send his wife back, in essence illegally, to pick up the portable, the packable . . . why?

Lots of debate. Three possibilities emerged:

1) He wasn't a *Fizl* but simply a Fool. In Austria, he fell victim to a fatal attack of Foolery, but not so much as to forego his collapsible stuff . . . His Native Soil was not native enough, without all his stuff.

"But why," protested Eva, "wouldn't somebody who wears a bow tie, someone who wears custom-made suits and makes himself out to be a gentleman, wouldn't he send his wife and son home and set out himself illegally to salvage his stuff?"

"Remember those precisely placed bedroom slippers, though!" said my wife.

"No gentleman," said Hanka, "Comrade family tyrant." So maybe it does figure, psychologically.

But what didn't figure was that if they hadn't meant to return to Prague, why had they given up their apartment?

"Cheapskate," said Eva. "Three months' storage is less than three months' rent."

"If he was a cheapskate, why ship the car? Round trip, if they intended to return to Canada?"

"He probably calculated that the freight costs would be twenty bucks less than renting a car."

All together then, if you stretched a few minor points, the hypothesis that The Fool Was No *Fizl* could fly. Of course, the women didn't believe it, so I came up with a second hypothesis;

2) He wasn't a Fool, he was a *Fizl*. Everything under the first hypothesis would stand up to scrutiny if Milena hadn't known that her husband was a *fizl*. And everything that didn't figure was camouflage so nobody would guess. He returned to Europe already intending to return to headquarters. She went there thinking that at best they might catch a glimpse of their Native Soil. But someplace they ran into one

of his contacts, she overheard something that made her put two and two together, or else maybe he even told her himself when they got to the border. And that was a shock, so much of a shock that she couldn't go back with him. For that matter, it's even possible that there was no stuff left in storage. He could have sent everything off behind her back, and Milena invented the storage story to somehow explain her solo return to Canada, and not have to admit that he was a *fizl.*

"Too much heavy-duty thinking for a little chickie like her," declared Eva. "Besides, she'd never have let the kid go with him."

Not very convincing.

And then there was a third hypothesis, one that I found unacceptable:

3) They are both *fizls.* He had returned to report in and get new orders, and she was supposed to tell everyone that he'd taken a contract job in France for six months and that he had put the boy in the Sorbonne for six months, on account of the French language—not unheard of here in Canada.

But a lot of things didn't figure.

Like if she was supposed to tell everyone, why hadn't she stuck to that story with us?

Why had they let the apartment go?

And why, why had it taken such a toll on Milena?

A peculiar sorrow came over me, a painful sorrow. "It's probably too much for her, chickie," said Eva. "Her nerves couldn't take it. Maybe they promoted her to some kind of lieutenant *fizl* and gave her a job of her own to do, and she couldn't hack it."

Manifest nonsense, in spite of the fact that Eva is smart. It's possible, but improbable. No, the most probable, still, is option number two. Except the women still wouldn't buy it.

And Milena—unwitting helper, or part of a smoke-screen? I don't know. That's what's the worst about the *fizl* system, and the persistent sorrow of the autumn that followed the summer. Nobody there knows who is who. There, you can't trust old friends, sweethearts or maybe even husbands, and because the absurdity of everybody's *fizling* on everybody expands geometrically, perhaps even parents and children. But sometimes I think to myself, "Just what is it they want to find out? And if everyone is truly the object of other people's *fizling*, doesn't it all cancel itself out? Or is it all just a myth? Yes, and no. The way it usually is, in myths. They say it's based on the principle of large numbers (and also on the extravagance of a country's inexhaustible means). Somewhere, perhaps in the tile tower, they must have huge archives, a veritable Himalayan mountain range of *fizl* reports (maybe they file them on microfilm; but then, I should think they'd use up the daily production of Kodak's Rochester factory or more for a day's worth of files. They're even said to have a letter-reading machine, made in Japan. A transparent moving belt, the postwoman, a *fizl* corporal, places letters, still sealed, on the belt after sorting them out of the mail traffic on the basis of lists. It had long since ceased to be a simple operation with a kettle of boiling water, steam, and gum arabic. Now, it's a Japanese letter-reading machine (was it a legend? Or a new triumph of progressive technology?). The belt, they say, doesn't move at a constant rate. Every quarter of a second, it gives a twitch. Beneath it is a strong light source and above it an automatic camera, its shutter synchronized with the light. Inside the lens, a cybernetic transfocator (Sci-fi? Legend? Reality?). In its sealed envelope, the letter twitches its way under the camera. The strong light illuminates it from below. The cybernetics calculates the thickness of the folded pages, communicates the data to the transfocator, in the next second or so, the camera takes the requisite number of pictures, with the transfocator adjusting the focus by a fraction of a millimeter. The result is a jigsaw puzzle, a jigsaw puzzle for *fizls*, which they tuck away in your file on microfilm. Then it just sits there, waiting for a rainy day. Legend says that only about one percent of them ever see that day. Not like Hemingway's iceberg, more like Faulkner's head of a pin. But the pin is stuck atop the Himalayas and is used for pricking. Once when I was editor in the Anglo-American section of Odeon publishers—and I was still young enough to believe that a person justifies his existence by the usefulness of his labor, this was how the hypnosis of war and Marxism had influenced me, that the old values were no longer good enough, I used to proofread Victorian novels, here and there I'd correct a typographical error, here and there a comma (though I was never quite certain of those), occasionally I would replace a redundant *which* with a *that*, and vice versa. After 800 pages and four working days over *David Copperfield*, I would feel something like a hangover: maybe twenty times *which* for *that*, three dozen commas, a couple of hundred typos (not to mention the ones that slipped by me!). What would have happened to David Copperfield without my twenty times *which* for *that* or vice versa? What would have happened, if anything? Would he have been diminished? Would he have said less about life, temporal or eternal? That hangover kept recurring, gnawing away at me: redundancy, well-paid (but not all that well) redundancy. And what about the creators of pinheads for the Himalayan peaks? It's supposed to pay off, though. One usable percent weighs more heavily than mountains of debris. It's scientific, like splitting atoms. And it's a fact, I can attest to it.

But first, how political schooling can hypnotize. A dangerous thing if you're young, undamaged, if you still feel that the most important thing is to JOIN FORCES WITH OTHERS to change the world and eradicate all the badness (when the truth is that anything you can do has to be done as an individual, only alone, and only within your immediate environs or, if you're really lucky, within the range of your audience, and then, you can't really change the world, at best you can mend it, and even so, good people will improve, and bad ones don't read literature). Dangerous indeed. I was young, already primed by Benno (if Benno can, son of a rich man, why not me, son of a white-collar worker?), and there, facing us at the political schooling lecture in the lovely little hotel stood a magical hypnotist with the hands of a laborer and a canny eloquence. What was fantastic about him (and hypnotic, too), in those days of prefabricated, modular clichés, was that he spoke in his own words. He had a talent for translating hackneyed phrases into ordinary language, in fact, into the local Eastern Bohemian idiom, the talent of a writer, the essence of writing. There I was, young, primed by Benno, with the scruples of bourgeois kids, their social consciences over-stimulated by the reverend fathers, and I listened to that articulate ex-laborer, and that ex-laborer explained, "It's not a matter of telling tales. It's a matter of comradely, collective help. If we want to help—and we truly do, we want to help everyone, indiscriminately—we have to know, and understand. Everyone has different faces that he shows to different people, without even realizing it. We need to know all those faces, and by projecting them simultaneously onto a single screen, we can assemble every comrade's genuine, inner countenance. We'll recognize what troubles him, where his uncertainties lie, and we'll be able to help him." I felt a profound yearning for help, everything troubled me, and despite having been primed by the ingenuous Benno, I was certain of nothing. "I'll pass around some questionnaires," said the ex-laborer, "You'll take one for each of your fellow teachers at the school. And you'll take them and fill each of them out, anonymously, of course, so you shouldn't feel hampered by any (absolutely ground-less) fear that the comrade might find out what you've written, and you'll write down, without reservations, the pure and complete truth, as you perceive it, that's the only way you can help." I took the forms and, primed and hypnotized, wanting to help and wanting to be helped, I penned horrible truths, itemized, without reservations. The faculty at the school where I taught, probably a typical one, consisted of a group of committedly intractable non-Marxists. Of course, practically everyone was a Party member, perhaps the only ones who weren't were the music teacher and me. Teachers are the vanguard, they are all supposed to be in the Party, their livelihoods depend on it. Yet I was amazed by their astonishing immunity to science, in particular to the Science of sciences. To them, it was all asinine: the exploitation of the working class, the privation of the proletariat, surplus value, to each according to his need, socialism, absolutely everything. I couldn't understand it. Today, I do, I see that it was just this irrational immunity that saved us, that under (the new) broad-scale humanism, (the old) small-scale humanism had not quite died out. Perhaps. But at the time, the flames of idealism were licking at my heels, I wasn't on fire yet, just beginning to kindle: "Málek, Josef, schoolteacher," I wrote. And I proceeded to mete out item after item. "A comrade without the foggiest notion of what it's all about." Yes, I laid it on: "He still believes in God, no, in a god. He tells political jokes." Criminal hypnosis. Under that muddling of minds—perhaps they had put something in the hotel coffee, too—I turned into an abominable Morozov,[83] a phantasmagoric monster. Hypnotized as I was by the canny antifascist with the working-man's hands and the gift of the language, if they had come to me and handed me an application to join the Party, I would have signed up on the spot.

Fortunately, Comrade Canny had made a mistake. He had distributed the questionnaires before lunch, to be filled out over the break, and as I sat on a bench in front of the hotel, dispensing incriminating truths, all of them absolutely truthful and all of them—though I didn't realize it at the time—grounds for dismissal, grounds indeed for arrest and imprisonment, all of a sudden, the hypnotic voice in my head began to fade, the hypnosis began to dwindle, the way alcohol (maybe there really was something in the coffee) evaporates, my writing slowed down, the worm of alcohol-induced (drug-induced, mass-suggested) certainty gradually spun itself into a cocoon, and the head that poked out of the cocoon was that of the beautiful butterfly princess. Uncertainty, she sneezed in the sunlight, and I was overcome with the writerly need to stop for a while, to read something, a comrade happened to be walking past with several copies of the latest *Rudé Právo*, he gave me one, I opened it and—that instant of all instants, perhaps all that is left of religion: at a moment of elemental crisis or the bleakest of despair, something happens that appears for all the world to be coincidence, someone calls, a sentence on a page of a randomly opened book catches your eye and deflects the crisis, a letter arrives, something happens, an absurd God working in an absurd way, *credo quia ridiculum*—my eye fell on a headline in *Rudé Právo*: SUBVERSIVE GROUP SENTENCED. Members of the Boy Scout movement. And they doled it out, the way I had to my colleagues (Málek, Josef taught singing, and singing was probably the only quality thing taught at that awful school, the geography teacher taught that in Canada, people speak Canadian, but Málek's children's chorus sang in tune, the children's voices of the spheres): Jarmila Ebenová, born 1932 (my moment of temptation, even more dangerous than the temptation of St. Aloisius, by the plump bosom of an unchaste phantasm), 15 years in prison; Jiří Kořínek, born 1933, 20 years; Dagmar Želivská, born 1932, 10 years. The year was 1950, before I ever heard of the unmarked graves, the curtain had yet to rise on the bizarre vaudeville that would be the Slánský trial. But through the fog of the imposed ideology, certain events began to crystallize, events that had happened earlier, in Kostelec, events I had barely registered, back then, in my youthful diffidence: Ruda Mach, arrested as an army officer, sentenced to 18 years; Benda's benign face by the swimming pool called Jericho: "Soon as I was behind bars, first thing, I got busted in the snoot!" They cast some light on the Science, the insistent willingness to help; it was as if I had suddenly leaped out of a mud bath and stood there naked, muddy, surrounded by people with their clothes on. In fact, I actually shivered, I picked up the forms bearing my unfinished comradely help (help for sure, comrades indeed, but which ones, which comrades?) and departed in the direction of the room that is significant in all dictatorships, i.e., the toilet, where you chuck love letters that could land you in the clink, and foreign currency and address books, because if they were to find anything like that on you during a search, say, at the border, they could turn you around and send you back, even if your trip were paid for in full and you have every possible clearance (what treasure troves the toilets in border-town taverns must be for the science of snooping; maybe they've even come up with a machine for salvaging soaked and flushed notebooks); I locked myself in there, amidst the last bit of privacy left in dictatorships (not even that, though, my friend Kathryn once discovered a little microphone under the rim of the toilet bowl in her room at the Hotel

Kiev in Moscow, an example of the concrete music of the
KGB, the only modernistic music in the U.S.S.R.) and I took
out some matches and set fire to my perfidious efforts to
help the comrades, because my formative years spent under
dictatorships had planted in me a gnawing uncertainty, I
wasn't even sure whether the teachings, the Science of
sciences, hadn't come up with a method whereby even torn-
up shreds of urine-soaked paper could be extracted, recom-
bined, smoothed and deciphered, thus ensuring that despite
the best efforts of a paper-tearing, urinating reactionary
spoiler of their helpful intentions, the comrades WOULD be
helped, willy-nilly, so I burned the papers to ashes, and after
I had stirred up the crumbled ashes in the toilet bowl with
the rolled-up *Rudé Právo*, I pulled down my trousers and shit
on it all, using the dry part of the *Rudé Právo* to wipe myself
(naturally, there was no toilet paper, which isn't an anti-
quated joke but a bare-assed reality) and then I flushed it all
down the drain, which fortunately wasn't plugged up the
way it usually was. Having undergone this ritual of purifica-
tion, I returned to the empty classroom, picked up a clean
set of questionnaires and proceeded to fill them with personal observations about my colleagues that glowed with
the uniform countenance of Exemplary Comrade with Positive Outlook, I lied like a rug, and the comrades could take
it all and stick it where the sun don't shine. As the Reverend
Father Meloun once declared, taking pen in hand to forge
an entry in the parish register about a marriage between an
Aryan lad and a Jewish bride: "Under certain circumstances,
an act of deception can become an act of Christian charity."
I had deceived the comrades, the worse comrade I. I was

sure that all my colleagues had described one another the same way, with a Positive Outlook, but then, of course, I could easily be wrong. Not everyone would have happened onto the *Rudé Právo* in the nick of time. Who knows. Who knows.

But what I wanted was to testify to the usefulness of the head of a pin. It was much, much later that my wife—handicapped by a brother in prison (fifteen years, for guiding two Boy Scouts illegally across the border, he had crossed back, good scout that he was, because his father was behind bars—two years for resisting officers of the People's Police in the act of nationalizing his bookstore—and because his mother was unemployed due to her husband's resisting officers of the People's Police), and a father who had defected to the United States after he got out of prison—was prohibited from traveling abroad, which made her practically useless to the folk ensemble where she was employed as a singer. Someone suggested that I drop in at the Ministry of the Interior and "explain" the situation to them. I still hadn't lost my faith in the scientific schooling of the People's Police officers or better said: I assumed that they appreciated a duality of countenance, the public face and the private face, and that if I were to explain my wife to them in terms of the schooling, they would have to respect the law (unwritten, or perhaps even written) of the society that called itself a *people's democracy*, and reassess the Person Thus Explained as a Reliable Person. So I sat down with the comrade with the expressionless face—on which even his manifest professionalism (which gave it its lack of expression) failed to generate the slightest appearance of intelligence (although it did occur to me that perhaps even that was professional mimicry)—and I explained my wife, according to the schooling, as a product of the Great World Depression, during which her father, the *failed* bookseller, was *unemployed*, and had to place her, as an *undernourished child*, in a *home for poor children* (I did neglect to mention the fact that the *home* was named after Tomáš Masaryk), her mother supported the family by *sewing aprons at home*, half a crown a piece—when he interrupted me: "We know all about that one, she's nothing but an old reactionary!" And so I did a lateral shift and proceeded to explain the mother in terms of the teaching: daughter of a *coal miner* and a *kitchen maid*, married a man who during the Depression was *unemployed*, during the Nazi occupation was a *political prisoner*, after the Victory of the People, in a *correctional facility*. She had no *education*, could not *understand*, life was *too difficult*, in fact, she was a Proletarian Mother, how could she be expected to *understand*, when in her *individual case* a *number of accidental coincidences*, the *bitter experiences* of having an *unemployed* husband, being the daughter of a *coal miner* and wife of a *political prisoner* under the Nazis, having two of her *children perish of malnutrition* during the Depression—at which point another comrade walked in with a file folder, my confessor buried his nose in it, turning pages while I continued explaining the mother according to the teaching, *bourgeois society* did not allow her an *education*, she *needs our help*, she is a *potential ally*, in fact, a *proletarian wo*—when the comrade stopped me cold, saying, "And so how come it says here black on white that on the third of May, nineteen hundred and fifty-eight, she was heard to say, in the Pramen produce market on Vítkova Street, that our Comrade President is an ass?"

He glared at me triumphantly. The Teaching collapsed, I never finished explaining her mother, and my wife didn't get to travel anywhere that time. A tiny pin stashed atop the Himalayas proved its usefulness.

So—unwittingly, or maybe as part of a smoke screen—Milena kept coming to us for solace, she brought me sorrow (why sorrow? But then, what's to be joyful about?), the rings under her eyes intensified, she would read to us from The Fool's letters (such sorrow, such sorrow): still no job, seeing bureaucrats, trying to get the kid into architecture at the university, trying to get her travel permit extended, she wept, the kid's drinking beer with his buddies but he writes her asking for a University of Toronto T-shirt, records by the current rock superstar, and even some kind of after-shave and a book about American astronauts, she wept, she didn't want to go back (she had rented a bachelor apartment in the neighboring high-rise), she got tipsy, Milena, I felt sorry for her.

I also got a letter from Kostelec. It wasn't from my Old Buddy but from Detective Babočka, another stroller from the promenade, an amazing phenomenon, apparently a genius, the kind you sometimes find in small towns, lost, or perhaps just sheltered there, a thinker, a philosopher, was he an eccentric after the fashion of the ecstatic hermits of our mountains or an Einstein without the Jewish chutzpah to set out from a small town to a big city in the treacherous world, I don't know. An electrician. At sixteen, he had mastered criminology (his nickname Detective Babočka was coined

by Přema), at eighteen, Russell's symbolic logic, now he
was a laborer in a factory for electrical goods, a photo fell
out of the envelope, on it Babočka with his two butterballs
(wife and daughter) and some old guy, all of them with
glasses raised in a toast. On the reverse: *"Přema at our place,
before returning to Australia."* That old fellow? No kidding.
The narrow Asian face, the toothless smile, the stubble of
grey hair, but those sorrowful eyes, the sorrow spread to
Toronto. Back to Australia. Babočka wrote:

> *He spent two years working in a foundry, and then he began
> getting drunk. Drowning something inside himself, sorrow
> and anguish. Isn't it strange? In principle, he's a communist
> and he up and leaves, but something was eating him, God
> knows what. . . .*

And delicately woven through the letter was a satire on life
in the land of overworked *fizls*, a satire for which its author
couldn't be criminally charged, because it registered the
obvious advantages (an oblation to pay for the satire? But
no less true for that.) as the sum total of entries on a balance
sheet, those sad signals flashed through my mind, *"working
up to my waist . . . they want younger guys . . . to Guinea, it's
better . . ."* and the sorrow of the Toronto night lit up with
the image of that night at the transmitter, broadcasting
mixed feelings into the ether, the one-armed legionnaire,
the modern Luddite, dismantling machinery, tossing parts
into the lovely Ledhuje River, the river of a simple, beautiful (beautiful? simple?) youth . . . a leap through the
window, a leap from a boat, that virgin, that soldier, that

splendid partisan of the age of simplicity, in principle, the last—

What does it mean, Babočka's detective story?

Time passed, and the day before Christmas Eve, Milena showed up. Tears engulfed the black circles under her eyes.

"Well, I got it."

"What?"

"The permit. But just till the end of the year. So I'm leaving—people!" It was like a cry, crying out to the people of the world (And sorrow. And me, sentimental fool. Me?). Tears dribbled onto her fur jacket. "People, will you hold it against me, that I'm going back there?" The options collapsed—what if she was speaking the truth? What if this least probable of possibilities was indeed the truth? I was overcome with sadness, at how life, the process of our ruination, cracks the mosaic of youth, making possible such uncertainty.

"Of course not, Milena! You have a husband and a son there! Nobody could hold anything against you. It would be inhuman to stay here, when—" We plied her with liquor, we consoled her, she spoke in the wavering voice of an old crone.

"I know," she turned to my wife, "that Karel did a stupid thing, but how can I—"

"Of course you can't, Milena, clearly—"

We walked her downstairs in front of the building. There, the emotional farewell. Hands clasped, kisses. Then she said, "And say, people—if Karel comes back—they wrote him that Toronto City Hall wants him to come and finish the project—if they let him go, can he stay over with you that first night, before he gets a place of his own?"

For God's sake, why is she saying that? My awful sorrow intensified. What is this? Does she believe it herself? Or is she building a foundation for a future explanation of an impossible return? And if it is such a foundation, is she in on it? Or is she simply naively repeating (this girl from the mosaic of Kostelec) the ruse tossed to her in a letter from atop the Himalayas?

I refused to believe what the facts were telling me to believe, the mind always manufactures a convenient solution if it wants one. Not a ruse, apparently just a fervent wish. The shining silhouette of Hradčany Castle, my cottage, the Vltava River dimmed, and a different light emerged in the memory of The Fool: the intersection of Bloor and Yonge, Casa Loma (stomp), sailboats with white sails, hazy Buffalo gradually emerging from Lake Ontario, the land of Indian tribes . . . Chingashook . . . I will return. No. Milena was telling the truth. It's just The Fool, just the eternal Fool with his East-West nostalgia, caught in Eliáš's cell.

Be that as it may, when someone knocked at our door three weeks later, all possibility of his return had slipped my mind, especially since I had never believed in it in the first place. My wife went to the door and, framed in the doorway—Yes! THE FOOL! The Fool—maybe it's a law of nature—dressed in a leather coat like the Gestapo used to wear, apparently from Saks Fifth Avenue—here to arrest us?—his little hat similarly evocative, his little head with the blond hair (when he removed the hat) brushed to one side, his little eyes looking down to where my wife stood, her mouth half open: "Well, I've come back again!" in a mushy voice (for the second time, I fully comprehended the meaning of the word *mushy*), the leather coat opened its arms, embraced my wife, and pressed a Judas kiss to her cheek (she turned her face just in time, and the full significance of "kiss of Judas" struck me right in the face).

My wife, having undergone a school of far harder knocks than I ever had, said, "Don't you tell me anything, Pavlas!"

"What? What? What?" exclaimed Pavlas, from Fool to *Fizl*, sat down at the table, his sentimental gaze flitting nervously, "How is your publishing house going? How many readers? And expenses? And profits?" The disconcerted *fizl* was automatically planting *fizl* questions, with no insulation between them, maybe just an amateur *fizl*—yes, the mind, when it wants to, keeps seeking ways to prevent the mosaic of youth from cracking wide open—maybe by his leap back to his Native Soil, he leapt into the *fizls'* net, maybe it wasn't until he needed to trade something for his son's acceptance at the faculty of architecture (the day before Christmas Eve, Milena had told us that's when the kid had gotten in, it had taken a lot of doing. Doing? What kind of doing?), oh no, not before that, not the whole time, this is his first *fizl* escapade, but why Toronto? It didn't figure, it just didn't figure.

"They let you go?" (that was me, asking).

"Oh, they're letting people go again. Things are all okay now, more or less. Anyone with a job offer in the West they'll let go now." He was telling fairy tales but blood will tell, it rose to his cheeks, and he continued with his automatic questions: "Where all do you have readers? Who does your editing? How come you don't own a house? You must have lots of money by now!"

"And where have you got a job, Pavlas?" (that was my wife).

"Why, at City Hall."

"So you say everything is okay, right, Pavlas?"

"Well—not everything. But—almost everything."

"Are they arresting people?"

"Not really." (Everything is okay. Sometimes a simple lie, sometimes a selfish phrase. I'll never forget: The phone rang. "Is it you?" A girlish voice with the sweet accents of Prague and the sixties, the voice of youths and maidens from what they called "the hydepark" beneath the statue of the saint who'd been burned at the stake, in the spring sunshine, the voice of a Czech girl. "I'm to say hi from Jirka Štajdl." "And who—are you?" She explained candidly. A Swiss citizen, mother a Czech, father Swiss German, a diplomat in Prague, studying in Prague and dating Jirka Štajdl—which sparked another recollection: the Chelsea Hotel, Miloš half asleep as usual, and in the pseudo-cynical manner of Americans, some Texas Czech is telling how the day before in Munich, he had talked with Štajdl, about Karel Gott, "Man, what a nut, interview upon interview, in one he said he'd never go back to Czechoslovakia, right after that he held another one in which he took it all back, in a third one he says he won't go back, man," snickers the Texas Czech, "you should of been there."[84] Back home in Toronto, a letter from Štajdl [may he rest in peace], asking if I knew about a teaching job at some university for a Czech lyricist, poet, and he enclosed a book about Karel Gott published in Prague in the age of very disconcerted *fizls*, would we consider publishing it? It might be interesting—After that, dead silence everywhere, and then new lyrics in *Melodies for the New Season*[85]—well, and now this one is dating Jirka Štajdl and Jirka says hi. "And—and how are things?" I ask. "What's he doing, Jirka? And Karel?" "Everything is okay again," I can picture her like a strawberry lily in the shade of the black statue of the saint [later I got a letter from my nephew, in an entirely different context, "That Štajdl has all the luck. First figure skater Hanka Mašková, and now he has a chick from an embassy, a veritable Rachel Velsh."]. "Everything is okay again," says the Rachel Welsh of Prague. "Karel has money again, they're not censoring Jirka's song lyrics all that much, they're singing on the radio and even on TV again."—"And what about Marta?" I interrupted the young Rachel. "Marta?" "Kubišová, of course!"[86] "Oh, her. Well, she's still blacklisted," says the young Rachel.) Yeah, everything is okay again, you old whore of a world with your short memory, that indifference that is our mother, our salvation, our ruin (this key sentence: *The Emöke Legend*), the *Fizl* Fool Pavlas sat there blushing, prying, snooping, an getting F-all.

"Sorry, we're invited to a party, we have to go," said my wife. It was two in the afternoon.

"Where to?" the *fizl* couldn't help asking.

"Actually, it's a wedding," said my wife.

"Who's getting married?"

"Some woman."

He left, we sat down to the phone. To warn friends, one after another as they appear in an exile's precious possession, his address book.

The next day, the *Fizl* Fool Pavlas attended a concert of the Toronto Symphony (Ančerl forewarned). After the concert, he went backstage to brown-nose the conductor. "Master! It was SPLENDID!" in his mushy voice. "HEAVENLY!" (He actually used adjectives like that.) "That THIRD MOVEMENT! Those HORNS! You have to forgive Milena, she couldn't come, she's laid up with the flu."

Mrs. Ančerl, Hana, came in: "Mr. Pavlas! I thought you were in Prague?"

The *Fizl* Fool blushed and stammered, "Wh-ho told you that? Who told you?"

"It's all over Toronto." He caught his breath (I registered the meaning of that idiom, too), he jumped up and out the door.

The next day, Járinka slammed the door in his face. The third day Eva phoned: He'd been at City Hall. Williams had been warned though, and greeted him with true Canadian candor: "But Mr. Pavlas, I heard you are working for the Czech Secret Police. So you'll understand, of course, that I can't give you your job back." He vacated the premises. He ran into similar reactions everywhere except at Guderna's, who hadn't been home when the warning calls were being made, and then he slipped our mind. He hadn't even known that Pavlas had gone back to Prague, painters live in their own world, and so he had to endure the *fizl*'s interrogation.

"How is it going, Master? The TEXTURE! The IMAGINATION!" That evening, probably sensing it, Járinka called Guderna. When he found out, the telephone receiver communicated sounds of an impending heart attack. So now they probably know just who in Toronto owns Guderna's paintings. What kind of a head of a pin they can construct out of that, I can't tell. I don't know.

We held another conference, because it just didn't figure at all. Are they truly that naive? "They've got to be able to figure out that we'll figure out what's what," said Eva, "even if they can't count past ten. He'll be suspect to everyone, and a suspect *fizl* is more of a hindrance than a help." (Can't they count past ten? Maybe, like everything, it's a combination of stupidity and smarts; according to the principle of large numbers as applied to social phenomena, things have a way of balancing out. Leaking information from a secret Party meeting will pass, a mother's immortal statement about the President won't, and in the long run, on the balance sheet, not a whole lot happens either way.) We racked our brains. There is always an exception to every rule. Maybe in the mess back home a miracle happens and they'll let a post-invasion repatriate out into the pernicious West. *Quia absurdum*, perhaps.

In my sorrow, I came up with another hypothesis: Milena had messed everything up, but Pavlas had made it right. At least, in Prague he had. Milena was supposed to spread the word in Toronto about a short-term job in France, and Pavlas convinced his bosses that that's what she was spreading. So they let him go. They had no idea that Milena had fallen apart. Milena, the sorrow of a spent youth—

"All right," said Eva. "But what about Milena? Why did she go back to Prague? How will The Fool explain that in the 'tile tower?'"

No, it didn't figure.

It was a mystery.

And a bitter, vexing sorrow over a cracked mosaic, now burst wide open.

The *Fizl* Fool Pavlas vanished from Toronto's Czech community milieu. Somebody made good a rumor that he had been hired on at York University. But it was a false trail. The Fool had vanished.

"Well, he's probably working another city," declared Eva. "He's just moved on. He's flashing his bow tie at parties in Calgary or in Edmonton. Or Vancouver. There are Czechs everywhere and they don't know him."

Should we write there? Try and find him? I got an idea. I have a collection of married Czech girls, good emissaries. I wrote one of them in Sweden and sent her Pavlas's Prague phone number, Milena had scribbled it down for me in the throes of parting. The Swedish emissary was planning a trip for Easter.

In my mailbox, I found a letter from Australia. What was the Absurd God communicating to me now? Even before I opened it, I knew who it was from. The writing looked like someone had taken a sledgehammer to it. Old Buddy.

Old Buddy,

So here I am again greeting you from Australia. At home, they booted me out, make up my mind, they said, either British subject or a Czech citizen. Somebody reported that I said something critical at the factory and the police told me that I was an undesirable person unless I renounce being a British subject, but I didn't bite. If I'd of done it, they could easily have stuck me in the cooler for criticizing. The beer here ain't Pilsner but it ain't bad either. The stupid tea-guzzlers here are suspicious of me because I was home so long, don't wonder, the Communists don't have a monopoly on stupid-

*ity. As you know, Labour won the election over here and I'm
kind of glad because they're beginning to give some kind of
social security like we had fifty years ago, and here they're
just beginning. If only they could stop the inflation, though.
Imagine, while I was away from Australia, beer went up from
30¢ to 40¢ and a room like you used to have for your maid costs
me $15 a week and I'm going to have to start eating meat like
they do in Europe, only just enough to have a little taste. But
the weather here is fine, I bike straight from work to the beach
and nights in the tavern there's a lot of Czechs here. I'm probably going to get a vacation in August, six weeks so maybe
I'll go take a look at Indonesia or maybe Hawaii. Write me
sometime what's new with you and your wife.*

Your Old Buddy.

Right after that came one from the Swedish emissary.

Dear Doctor,

*As you asked, I dialed the number from a public phone
booth as you suggested, I talked through a hankie (on your
suggestion, too) and said, "Can I please talk with Mr.
Pavlas, the architect? My name is Procházková, and I
heard, sir, that you came back from Toronto, and I have a
guy there and he hasn't written to me in more than six
months, so I'm worried," and the architect interrupted me,
and he wasn't the least bit mushy the way you wrote he was:
"I was in Canada as a city planning specialist, and I never
had anything to do with any Czechs there!" And he hung
up on me. Considering how curt and abrupt he was, I
deduced that his phone was bugged, and I was kind of*

alarmed, what do you think, Doctor? Was that hankie enough? They're supposed to have voice analyzers already, I mean I disguised my voice, I spoke really high, but they say that kind of trick is just what they have the voice analyzers for. Please reassure your faithful, anxious messenger to our aging homeland.

Ludmila F. Olavsson

I sat over those two letters for a long time, while a neon rainbow spread across the Toronto sky on Yonge Street. A *fizl?* Or just another miracle in the mess of Czech stupidity? Would they send him out again? Where to? And what about Milena? Does she know? She knows. And she stays with him. Why not. The death of literature, the death of the lovely town of Kostelec. The Absurd God, who for reasons known only to Himself never speaks clearly, just in parallaxes. No, I mean in paradoxes. Or—I looked at the map of the world that my wife had tacked up on the wall to cheer herself up. Parallax—position is all in where you view it from. Those treks by ship or by jet, Kostelec–Darwin–Toronto–Prague. None of it makes sense, unless you have a sense of your vantage point. And in this world . . .

What is the sense of it? I don't know. None, maybe. I don't know, and of course it isn't important that I don't know. Outside my window, lights flicker in the vertical spires of St. James Town, my dream skyscrapers from the age of Dr. Mejzlík, the black man on the floor above sings the blues:

Shut up, double-talkin' mama, you know you done me wrong!

I say, shut up, you double-talkin' mama, you done me goddamn wrong!

I ain't got nuttin' left, jes' to sing dis song . . .

Magna Mater, world, mother of mine, you indifferent old whore. Neuilly, a quarter where they permanent-wave the lawns, streets, a movie theater, a scene from a film. Sylva, who by her return prolongs with all her might the unreal duration of the dream of the age of impotent *fizls*, pregnant mothers forgotten, gave birth are hanged, the infant dies, child support an eighteen-year labor of Sisyphus Estonian engineer 500-kilogram hog who would have guessed that even me. Even the Neuilly nights the vague visions strawberry Marie my wife true to an old promise crazy world frog run over on the bank of the lovely Ledhuje River.

This testimony.

translator's notes

1. *Children of Lidice—*
   In the aftermath of the World War II assassination of SS-Ober-gruppenführer Reinhard Heydrich by Czech and Slovak parachutists sent from England, the Nazis razed the mining village of Lidice, shot all the men, sent all the women to the Ravensbrück concentration camp, and placed the little children for adoption with childless German families. Very few of these abducted children were returned to their mothers after the war.

2. *Zoshchenko, Akhmatova, the Soviet Art Exhibition—*
   Soviet writers Mikhail Mikhailovich Zoshchenko and Anna Akhmatova were savagely attacked by Stalin's cultural henchman Zhdanov just before the opening of the Soviet Art Exhibition in Prague in 1947. For the first time, Czech artists were treated to a dose of socialist realism. Since most of them had been adherents of various modern movements, the exhibition came as a severe shock.

3. *B. Kolder, Alexander Dubček—*
   Kolder, together with Dubček, the reform-minded chairman of the Communist Party of Czechoslovakia, whose politics brought

about the Soviet ambush in August 1968, signed the Party document known as the Kolder Report. This report informed Party members about the inhuman treatment of political prisoners in the fifties. The document was soon leaked to the public.

4. *1948*—
The year of the Communist putsch that enthroned Stalinism in Czechoslovakia.

5. *Action Committee*—
Ad hoc Communist committees that were empowered to fire people from jobs and even to have them arrested, without giving them any reason.

6. Jenseits von Gut und Böse—
A book by German philosopher Friedrich Wilhelm Nietzsche proclaiming the categories of Good and Evil to be mere prejudices.

7. *No man is an island*—
Famous line from a poem by John Donne, an English poet of the seventeenth and eighteenth centuries. It was made popular by Ernest Hemingway, who used another line from the same poem to title his novel *For Whom the Bell Tolls*.

8. *President's funeral*—
The funeral of Edvard Beneš in the summer of 1948, which became the last mass demonstration against the Communist Party's grabbing of totalitarian power.

9. *Klement Gottwald*—
A Communist Member of Parliament both before and after World War II. After the 1948 putsch, he became president.

10. *He still cast his vote*—
The Communist regime proclaimed a new constitution in May

1948, only three months after the putsch. Many members of Parliament who had been elected before the putsch were still in Parliament, but they voted for the Constitution out of fear. They were all removed in the first Communist "elections" that soon followed: the "election with no selection."

11. *Black barons—*
Members of punitive military units where soldiers were posted if they were of the wrong class origin, political past or religious persuasion, including many clergymen.

12. *She has written it far better—*
Refers to the novel *Summer in Prague* by Zdena Salivarová.

13. *Lizetka—*
A prominent character in the author's book *The Tenor Saxophonist's Story.*

14. *Láďa—*
Ladislav Fuks, one of the most brilliant writers of the sixties who, after the Soviet ambush, was coerced into writing a couple of politically correct novels.

15. *Tile tower—*
The much-feared Ministry of Internal Security was housed in a tiled building on Letná Hill in Prague.

16. Fizls *(pronounced "feezles," rhymes with weasels)—*
The translator brings this Czech word into the book because there is no accurate equivalent in modern English. A *fizl* is an agent of the secret police, an informer, usually in a totalitarian state. The slang expression is filled with contempt and hatred.

17. When I swing by the string—
A female thief sentenced to the gallows sings this ditty in Daniel Defoe's *Moll Flanders.*

18. *Procession*—
Refers to the funeral procession at President Beneš's funeral.

19. *With the stern justice of men*—
A quotation from Hemingway's *A Farewell to Arms*.

20. *Dies irae, dies illa*—
The Last Judgment, from the thirteenth-century Latin hymn by Iacopone.

21. *The battlefront road is long*—
A popular song of Red Army frontline drivers.

22. *Legionnaire*—
Member of the Czech Legion in World War I Russia, an army of volunteers who fought the Bolsheviks.

23. *February*—
Refers to the Communist putsch in February 1948.

24. *Prisoner-cum-miner*—
A political prisoner whose prison sentence was spent in forced labor in uranium mines. After their release, many of them remained miners elsewhere.

25. *Falcons, Eagles*—
Names of patriotic physical training organizations—Eagles were Catholics, Falcons were nondenominational.

26. Maul halten und weiter dienen—
A notorious German military phrase which means, in essence, "Shut up and follow orders."

27. *Job placement chit*—
Graduates of educational institutions, including universities, were not free to find themselves jobs wherever they chose; they

were obliged to accept placement wherever the chits assigned
them.

28. *Young men in the blue shirts—*
Members of the Communist-led youth organization called the
Czechoslovak Youth Union. The blue shirts were their uniform.

29. *Mme Podolská—*
The most fashionable dressmaker in Prague.

30. *Sašenka—*
A female character in the author's *The Tenor Saxophonist's Story*.

31. *When I was attacked from all sides—*
After the publication of his first novel *The Cowards*, the author
was the target of an orchestrated Party campaign.

32. *The novel—*
Refers to the author's novel published in English as *Miss Silver's
Past*.

33. *Sorry Tony—*
After the Soviet invasion in 1968, young people started wearing
buttons with this inscription to express that however dreadful
life was under President Antonín (Tony) Novotný, whom they
helped to discredit, life under President Husák was much worse.

34. Because I do not hope—
Line from T.S. Eliot's "Ash-Wednesday."

35. *"Arrival of the armies"—*
Communist euphemism for the nocturnal Soviet ambush following the Prague Spring in 1968.

36. *On their Index—*
There was, of course, nothing literally called the Index under

Communism, but certain topics, e.g., criticism of the Party, or sex, were taboo.

37. And arresting them all—
From a sonnet by Jan Zábrana, friend of the author and co-author with him of some detective novels. He died prematurely in the mid-eighties.

38. *So after their son was rehabilitated*—
Under the impact of the first Thaw, some executed political "criminals" were posthumously pronounced innocent.

39. *The court that freed Angela*—
Reference to Angela Davis, the American Stalinist, member of the Central Committee of the Communist Party of the United States.

40. *Saša*—
A nickname for Alexander; this reference is to Alexander Dubček.

41. *Antago and non-antago*—
Refers to one of Mao Zedong's theories according to which contradictions of capitalism were "antagonistic," whereas contradictions of socialism were "non-antagonistic."

42. The doomsday machine of the revolution—
Quote from the author's novel *The Miracle Game*.

43. *The Tank Corps*—
Published in English as *The Republic of Whores*.

44. *Which Graham Greene didn't fail . . .* —
Refers to the passage from the novella "Emöke" "that indifference that is our mother, our salvation, our ruin," which Greene pointed out in a letter to the author.

45. I thought frantically—
Quotation from the author's novel *The Cowards*.

46. *Dr. Mejzlík*—
A humane criminal investigator in stories by Czech writer Karel Čapek. The figure is characteristic for Czech democracy between the two world wars.

47. *Barrandov*—
A favorite café on the hill called Barrandov in Prague, famous for its several terraces with dance floors.

48. *Eduard Haken*—
A famous basso from the National Theater Opera Company.

49. White blossoms all along—
Lyrics to the "Wedding Song" from Antonín Dvořák's opera *Rusalka* (known in English as *The Water Nymph*).

50. That beautiful detachment—
Quote from Hemingway's *A Farewell to Arms*.

51. To dogs, a dog's death—
A pronouncement of the Stalinist poet Ivan Skála after the antisemitic Slánský trials in 1951, at which eleven defendants were sentenced to hang.

52. *Artur London*—
One of the few defendants at the Slánský trials who received "only" a life sentence. He later described his experience in a book of memoirs. (Filmed as "The Confession" by Costa Gavras.)

53. *Damaged the careers*—
The Communist establishment availed itself of the services of excellent non-Communist artists (e.g., Alfred and Emil Radok, the creators of the celebrated Magic Lantern Theater) for the

Brussels Expo in 1958. After having made a significant contribution to the success of the Czechoslovak Pavilion, upon their return home they were treated by the arts establishment as if they were suspect.

54. *Ludvík Vaculíks—*
Author of *The Guinea Pigs* and a leading dissident writer.

55. *Youth Union—*
The overtly apolitical but actually Communist-run youth organization.

56. *Class register—*
A permanent record used by high school teachers to register classroom records, reprimands, attendance, etc.

57. *Karel Čapek—*
Famous Czech author between the two world wars, died, some say of a broken heart, shortly after the Munich agreement. He is best known in the West for his plays *R.U.R.* (which gave the English language the word "robot") and *The War of the Newts*. The quotation is from his pioneering work *Marsyas, or on the Margins of Literature*, an exploration of what later was to become a legitimate subject of study: popular literature.

58. Politruks—
Political officers.

59. And when you show me a man—
Quote from Henry Miller's *Tropic of Cancer*.

60. *Milada Horáková—*
The only woman ever to be sentenced to death by her own people for so-called "political crimes." She was a Socialist Member of Parliament who, after the 1948 putsch, secretly met several times with her Socialist Party colleagues.

61. We travel to Moscow—
     An authentic pronouncement in pre-World War II Parliament,
     made by the Communist leader Klement Gottwald.

62. You're a danger—
     Quote from Graham Greene's *The Power and the Glory*.

63. *Former SS-men*—
     Denizens of the detention camp in Sicily were an incongruous
     group of people of various nationalities who (usually by choice)
     had no identification or passports, e.g., the *Ustachi* (Croatian
     gendarmes, many of whom had collaborated with the Nazis), or
     members of the army of General Vlasov who, as a POW, was
     persuaded by German Army authorities to organize a Russian
     Liberation Army that would fight against Stalin. Recruits were
     usually desperate POWs.

64. *General Alois Eliáš*—
     A general of the Czech legion in Russia, who after the Nazis oc-
     cupied Czechoslovakia accepted the role of Prime Minister of
     the Protectorate government. He continued to work with an
     underground network of anti-Nazi officers and was in regular
     wireless touch with the exiled President Beneš in London. After
     the assassination of Heydrich, Eliáš was executed, as he had
     known he would be.

65. *Biebl and Neumann*—
     Konstantin Biebl was a modern poet who committed suicide
     after the putsch of 1948. Stanislav Neumann did the same after
     the Soviet ambush in 1968.

66. *The munificent building of socialism*—
     Reference to the rather remarkable poet, playwright and novel-
     ist Pavel Kohout, who went from Anglophile to Stalinist to Re-
     form Communist to Socialist to—the author hasn't kept up on
     his comings and goings lately. The line *"the caterpillar slithers*

aboard" is from his ode to the Allied invasion of France, written for choral recitation.

67. *Songs by a contemporary bard*—
Jiří Suchý, author of song lyrics, playwright-actor-singer-comic whose lyrics, untainted by cliché, helped greatly to make the official, cliché-ridden songwriting look ridiculous.

68. *Yonge and Bloor*—
The intersection of two main downtown Toronto streets.

69. *Those who can, do*—
Paraphrase of a sentence in William Faulkner's *The Unvanquished.*

70. Evening Songs—
A book of poems by mid-nineteenth-century poet Vítězslav Hálek, who is now largely forgotten.

71. Tales from the Lesser Quarter—
A book of short stories by nineteenth-century writer Jan Neruda that has become a Czech literary classic.

72. *Dudintsev*—
A Russian writer of the Thaw severely attacked by Party hacks and eventually exonerated by Khrushchev.

73. *Jirka Šlitr*—
Composer of songs, partner to Suchý, the most popular songwriting pair of the sixties. Died tragically after the Soviet ambush.

74. *Fikar, Grossman, etc.*—
Important personalities of Czech cultural life in the sixties: Ladislav Fikar, poet, film producer, and editor who published the author's *Cowards* and greatly contributed to the Czech New Wave in the cinema; Jan Grossman, dramaturge and director of

all Havel's plays in the theater on the Balustrade in Prague; Josef
Hiršal, poet and excellent translator of poetry; Jiří Lederer, a
leading journalist.

75. *Vráťa Blažek*—
Leading author of stage and film comedies, writer of song lyrics,
and author's childhood friend, portrayed in *The Engineer of
Human Souls* as Vratislav Blažej.

76. *Eminent professor of the Czech language*—
Literary gossip has it that lexicographer Professor František
Trávníček was the model for the stupid and arrogant Lieutenant
Dub in Jaroslav Hašek's *The Good Soldier Švejk* (also translated as
The Good Soldier Schweik).

77. *Václav Černý*—
Eminent non-Communist literary scholar, discoverer of unknown manuscripts of Lope de Vega; for most of his life he was
banned from the University by the Communist regime and
eventually became one of the most prominent dissidents after the
Soviet ambush of 1968. He died before the fall of Communism.

78. *Ivan Passer*—
Czech–American film director (*Intimate Lighting*, *Law and Disor-
der*, *Cutter's Way*).

79. *Vixi*—
A leading female character in *The Miracle Game*.

80. *UAC, GDR, IWD*—
United Agricultural Cooperative (UAC); The German Demo-
cratic Republic (GDR) (East Germany); International Women's
Day (IWD).

81. *The teaching of all teachings*—
Stock Party phrase for Marxism-Leninism.

82. *František Halas*—
One of the most important Czech poets, a Catholic and a Communist at the same time; "I Shall Return Home" is a lyrical prose ode to his native region.

83. *Abominable Morozov*—
A Soviet boy, enthusiastic member of the Young Communist League, who informed on his own father who was then executed. A group of the father's friends then killed the boy, and he became a legend in Stalinist lore.

84. *Jirka Štajdl . . . Karel Gott*—
A year after the Soviet ambush, famous pop singer Karel Gott was touring West Germany when he decided to stay in the West, then changed his decision several times and eventually returned to Prague. Jiří (Jirka) Štajdl was Gott's lyricist and Boswell; the whole scene took place in Miloš Forman's room in the old Chelsea Hotel in New York.

85. *"Melodies for the Next Season"*—
A popular Czechoslovakian TV show.

86. Marta Kubišová—
Most popular female pop singer before the 1968 Soviet ambush. Because she remained loyal to Dubček, she was blacklisted and was unable to sing publicly until 1989, the year Communism collapsed in Czechoslovakia.

the

tenor

saxophonist's

story

panta rei

You can't step in the same river twice.

Heraclitus

I N THOSE DAYS, I was only a baby fascist while my father was a big fascist, although he didn't think of himself like that. That's today's simplified way of putting it; in the old days these things were more complicated. I was a little bourgeois boy in velvet pants, with a polka-dot handkerchief tied under my chin, and I'd taunt Voženil: "Bolshevik, Bolshevik!" as I munched on my frankfurter. Voženil waited to see if I'd leave him a morsel, and when I didn't he called me "you pen-pushing greedy-gut" and I paid him back with "you Bolshevik." Each of us brought it from home: me with my velvet pants and suspenders decorated with airplanes and locomotives, Voženil with his big loud mouth that always gave off the sweet smell of bread (he never brushed his teeth), clodhoppers passed down from an older brother, dirty words which I never used because I knew from home that you weren't supposed to. Still, my father was a big, strong fascist, even though he didn't think of himself in that way. He marched in processions sporting a cane because he had a limp inherited from the First World War, and he wore a silver-gray shirt. I boasted about him to schoolmates and was very proud of him when I stood on the sidewalk with my mother, who held me by the hand, and we watched him striding down the street, we watched him scowl and sing and shout.

Once, however, I saw him weep, and I couldn't believe my own eyes. That was the time the Conservative leader Dr. Kramář died. Dad's large, meaty mouth which ground away at dinnertime like a millstone now collapsed into a crooked curve resembling the tragic semicircle painted on the lips of the great comedian George Voskovec (described by Dad as a drawing-room Bolshevik and agent of Moscow), tears rolled down his smooth-shaven cheeks, tears as big as the pearls in Mother's necklace but glassy, transparent and damp. Dad sat in the cool, darkened drawing room, with its violet wallpaper, black piano and black furniture; only the gilded face of the grandfather clock glowed in the dusk. Tears as big as pearls, as big as drops of autumn rain kept dropping off Dad's vest. Facing him sat Mrs. Zkoumal, editor of *Národní Listy*, dressed in a black silk gown, her red hair upswept into a mikado. Her elegant hands, with red-enameled nails that extended a good centimeter beyond the fingertips, kept kneading a black-bordered handkerchief.

She moaned: "What a man! What a mind! A real giant! What a Czech! They don't come any finer! And they kept hounding him all his life! Bolsheviks, the Beneš crowd, clericals, the Castle, all of them! All of them are guilty! They hounded him to his grave! To deprive the nation of such a man! But they'll soon see what they have wrought!"

I didn't understand what was going on, while I sat in a chair in a black velvet suit, my feet dangling high above the floor, Mother next to me, also wearing black, not weeping but looking sad. But then she always looked sad. I gazed in fascination at that red-gold-rust-colored mikado hairdo of Madam Editor, at her eyebrows as thin as a thread and arched like Gothic vaults in the church, her slender legs in silk stockings visible way past the knees because Madam Editor had her legs crossed and though her gown was a mourning gown it was also stylish, as could be expected from a youthful star on the *Národní Listy* editorial staff.

That was the first time I saw—and heard—Madam Editor.

Then a couple of years quickly went by and a lot happened. The Germans sent Dad to a concentration camp, because he took his nationalist convictions seriously. They took away our apartment and Mother moved us to Grandpa's house in the country.

One evening after the war, when I was already grown up, and had exchanged my velvet shorts for stylish close-cut trousers and played tenor sax in a jazz band, a man came to see us one evening and handed Mother a crumpled letter which Dad had given him in Oranienburg. Mother read it and started crying; she cried on and on—from that day on she turned ever sadder and in the end she stopped talking, only sat and stared. Then they took her to an insane asylum.

That man told us how he and Dad slept in the same bunk and helped each other as well as they could, though they also argued. They argued on account of bolshevism. Dad believed that the Czech nation would come to its senses after the war—meaning that the National Democratic party would take over the government—and he became furious when the man maintained that Comrade Stalin would see to it that things turned out differently. Dad was altogether naive. He even behaved insolently toward the SS troopers, and so in the end they did away with him.

After they took Mother to the asylum, Grandpa had a stroke and they kicked us out of the house. I moved to Prague, started to play tenor sax in Zetka's jazz band and became friends with Miss Julie Nedochodil, whose dad was a deputy of the Catholic Populist party. Not sensing anything wrong, he let me sublet a room in his beautiful modernist villa.

At his house I met Madam Editor for the second time.

She no longer wore a short gown, a red mikado hairdo nor long red claws on her fingers. She was dressed in a shapeless gray outfit, her feet were modestly ensconced in low-heeled shoes, her hair was set in nondescript waves and on her bosom—which was hard to make out under the guileless blouse—a gold cross. She was sitting in the dining room, where the conversation centered on materialism and spiritualism. She kept casting devout glances at Franciscan Father Urbanec and held forth:

"Such obvious nonsense," she said. "How can anybody believe such things? This world, this fascinating universe filled with heavenly wonders, this body of mine, all those amazing miracles of creation which proclaim the glory of the Creator—can this be nothing but dead, uncreative, motionless matter?"

Father Urbanec kept nodding his head while his hand nestled a cut-glass goblet in which a little puddle of yellow wine from the Teplá cloister rolled gently from side to side like a spoonful of honey. In the rays of the sun, filtered through the greenery of Papa Nedochodil's lush garden, it emanated a golden glow into the dining room. Father Urbanec was responsible for guiding converts and Madam Editor was his sheep. She converted totally. She switched from the banned *Národní Listy* to the still tolerated *Lidová Demokracie*. She took her son out of public high school and enrolled him in the archbishop's school in Dejvice. She also launched a battle for the soul of her husband, and managed to return him to the pale of the Church in the nick of time, as he lay on his deathbed. Before this long-suffering agnostic breathed his last, the rite of a church wedding was performed with the assistance of Father Urbanec, so that after fifteen years of civil cohabitation their marriage became sanctified before God. The place of Dr. Kramář in her heart was taken over by Father Urbanec. She even chose him as her confessor, and on the first Friday of every month pestered him with her sins, which she committed mainly in thought, less frequently in speech and hardly ever in action. She joined the Society of Perpetual Veneration of the Consecrated Host, and also the Eucharistic Society of Saint Cypriana for reclaiming young women as novices. She also became a leader of Catholic Girl Scouts. She thus became—or rather, remained—a fighter against bolshevism, albeit under a new flag.

From that day on, I saw her quite often. She was a constant visitor at Papa Nedochodil's, picking his brains for political ideas. She took a critical stance toward me, because I

favored wild neckties and striped socks and on Sundays, instead of going to church, I blew hot licks in a popular dance
joint in Vinohrady and elsewhere. She also criticized the virtually Bolshevik opinions of Pavel Nedochodil, a boy whom
his family considered something of a failure and who entered
the Young Communist Movement. She feared for our souls;
performed heroic apostolic labors left and right. She managed to bring Julie to the verge of tears when that attractive
Catholic girl bought herself a two-piece swimsuit; she got
Madam Nedochodil to cancel her subscription to *Kino*; and
she exerted such strong influence over Papa Nedochodil
that he stopped reading detective stories. She radiated sanc-
tity and deep faith.

Then a miracle happened in Slovakia: two shepherd
children in Malá Fatra had a vision of the Virgin Mary.
Madam Editor took off at once in search of miracle and
news story. She went in the company of journalists, consisting of cynics from the communist *Rudé Právo* and sensation-
seekers from *Svobodné Slovo*.

They came back a week later.

"You should have seen the cars, Doctor!" she reported
to a gathering that was headed by Papa Nedochodil and
Father Urbanec and that also included Julie with a somewhat uncatholically low-cut dress, and myself, sporting a
specially selected Bikini-Nagasaki necktie.

"Bumper-to-bumper traffic for miles! We had to get out
and walk, and only our newspaper passes got us through the
throngs. We reached the little hill where they had put up a
small, simple altar and at a quarter to three they brought the
two children. The Virgin was supposed to appear at four,

the hour of Christ's death. The children knelt and prayed, and that whole throng of hundreds and thousands knelt and prayed with them. Oh, Doctor! I've never experienced such a blissful feeling in my life! And then at four the children started to talk and we heard them asking questions and answering—we didn't see nor hear the Virgin but felt that she was there with us! And then a priest took the children away and as for myself—I can tell you, Doctor, I feel that I was present at a miracle!"

There was talk of visions and miracles, of Fatima, La Salette, Bernadette, stigmata, the holy shroud of Turin, and in the end, as usual, the conversation passed to the subject of communism and communists. Madam Editor recounted her experiences in this regard:

"It's a moral morass, Doctor! Those people lack the most basic moral sense! I am ashamed to talk about it, I really feel myself blushing—but I have to tell you what sort of people they are! Just imagine, Doctor! We spent the night in Bratislava in the Winston Hotel and the editors from *Rudé Právo*—well, you can imagine how they joked about the miracle! They blasphemed in a way I wouldn't dare to repeat. Right after dinner I went to my room—and . . . I really don't know if I can say it with Julie sitting right here . . ."

She nodded her head in the direction of the half-bared bosom of my companion, who responded with a grimace.

"But I'll say it straight out, so that all of you get the picture of that crowd. Just imagine, one of the *Rudé Právo* editors—a widower with two children—followed me and grabbed me upstairs in the hall—of course, he smelled like a brewery—and he wanted—no, I'm too ashamed—he wanted me—well, he wanted me to do his bidding! Doctor! Forgive me for saying it, under normal conditions such a thing would never pass my lips, I just want you to know with what sort of element we have the honor of dealing. And he made me a marriage proposal! But first he wanted . . . well, Doctor, that's bolshevism for you! In the afternoon, they witness an unforgettable moment on Malá Fatra and just a few hours later they're back in the gutter . . ."

Then came February.

Disaster.

They threw Papa Nedochodil out of Parliament and Madam Editor off the paper.

They gave her a job in a factory.

I was thrown off the faculty. I had to make my living playing the saxophone.

Pater Urbanec went to prison.

At first, Madam Editor came to see us almost every day seeking encouragement. Everything in the factory offended her. Vulgar jokes, immoral talk, coarse and dull work. "It's so mechanical, Doctor, so mechanical! There is absolutely no need for thought! And all my life I've worked with my mind!"

She was being broken into the job by an oldish foreman, a widower, who called her "girl" and made indecent proposals to her, such as inviting her out to the movies or to dances. Let's live a little, he'd say to her.

The Editor's horror knew no bounds.

Then Julie's older sister Tereza married a Protestant. Madam Editor kept wringing her hands and spent a week in churches (after work), kneeling and praying for poor Terezinka.

Some time later, I was sent to jail for two weeks for committing light physical damage, under the influence of alcohol, upon a certain youth who kept pawing Julie in places of her body that were out of bounds. When I got out, Madam Editor warned me that alcohol is bad for the health and arouses animal instincts, though in my case its effect was rather the opposite.

Strangely enough, I noticed that she didn't say a word about the soul or about morality.

Half a year later, Communist Youth member Pavel Nedochodil was elected as the Party's candidate. Madam Editor—whose visits to Papa Nedochodil had become much rarer—came one evening, and seemed to take the news in stride. For a while, she chatted about nothing in particular and then got on the subject of the factory, the need to understand those people, who actually aren't a bad sort, it's true they use immoral expressions but this is due to the fact that they had been deprived of a good education.

She didn't add "during the first, bourgeois republic," the standard phrase used by *Rudé Právo*, because she didn't dare go quite that far in the presence of Papa Nedochodil. I noticed that she wore a new dress, modestly high in front but at the same time quite close-fitting so that her bosom clearly outlined the space intended for it. Whatever she was like, Madam Editor certainly aroused sinful ideas. She also wore nylon stockings with black seams and white high-heeled shoes. She told us that the foreman—that widower—heehee—kept hinting that the two of them ought to get hitched—he says—heehee—he needs a good woman. He says a man without a woman is no man at all. Of course, she doesn't take any of that too seriously. But on her birthday he bought her—heehee—a handbag. An awful one, of course. He's got real low-brow taste. She didn't want to accept it, but he insisted and yesterday he even brought her—heehee—a bouquet of forget-me-nots . . .

After that, she stopped coming to Papa Nedochodil.

We heard various rumors.

We learned that she had moved in with that foreman and lived with him in one nest, as the expression goes.

And that she was getting active in the revolutionary workers' movement.

After that—well, after that there was no longer any interest in her at Papa Nedochodil's house.

Some more time passed, and in general I was getting along fine. I played tenor sax, and even had some female admirers.

I had a few smashing suits hanging in my closet, found a luxurious sublet on Rajský Hill in a villa of a former composer of hit songs for the Tyláček operetta company (who had made a timely switch to military marches and workers' choruses). I broke up with Miss Julie Nedochodil, who went on to marry a refrigerator repair man; and all in all, socialism suited me just fine.

One Sunday afternoon, in summer, as we were playing for a huge crowd in the Fučík Park of Rest and Relaxation, my throat was getting parched and during our break I got into line in front of a watermelon stand.

The attendant kept slicing the watery spheres with a rusty knife and slid the sections down a bare plank, where swarms of flies gaily copulated in the pink juice.

"Comrade!" I heard someone in back of me say, "Comrade! You ought to cover those boards with something, at least some wrapping paper! This is terribly unhygienic! And as a food handler you ought to wear a white coat! Not a sweaty shirt . . . It's not fair to your fellow comrades, comrade, to give them spoiled goods for their honestly earned money!"

I turned around.

My eyes nearly popped out of my head. I beheld a large, shining, five-point red star on the lapel of a modest yet elegant tailored dress.

In the dress stood Madam Editor.

I was sporting a jazzy white jacket and the hitch from my tenor sax was looped around my neck.

I thought it wiser to remain anonymous.

truths

What applies to all the members of a given class,
is true of each of them individually.

Syllogistic axiom

TAKE CERTAIN set phrases and expressions, like: "You made your bed, now lie in it." Or: "A man makes his own luck." When I hear such stuff, I could explode. Or things like: "Nation X is incensed by the behavior of Nation Y." Seriously, what kind of nonsense is that? Or: "The assembly unanimously approved . . ."

Unanimously. It would be interesting to find out what the various members really thought, if somebody could see inside their brains and write it up.

But nobody ever will. I tend to think that the world will always have its secret police, and consequently there will always be private opinions and unanimously approved opinions.

Not to mention so-called common-sense opinions.

Alas, ideal society, ideal society! What turns dream into nonsense? Why will nobody ever see you come into being?

Why are you as unattainable as a perpetual motion machine?

Of course, I shall never proclaim such thoughts publicly. I'm not that crazy.

As you know, ladies, the people who fare best in this world are usually the worst bastards. And if you insist on proof, you can kiss my you-know-what. Pardon me.

The only excuse for your naivete is the reformed school curriculum and the resulting ignorance of classical Greek. You don't even know what an axiom is. An axiom is a basic, completely self-evident judgment that confirms itself and needs no further proof.

In order to keep that definition firmly in your head, just remember this example of an axiom: the people who fare best in this world are usually the worst bastards.

These bastards are generally the most ardent proclaimers of truths. Truths don't bother them. Truths never knock them out or shake their guts.

Pardon me.

Let me give you just one such story about truth.

It happened at a time before they kicked me out of English and American Studies. I had volunteered to help out in the American Institute and in Friends of the USA, and I worked like a demon, not out of any love for capitalism—I had no strong feelings about that—but because I was bucking for a grant or fellowship that would enable me to visit that imperialist country and take in the likes of Mary Lou Williams with my own eyes and ears.

So when Uncle Sam's army decided to arrange weekly visits to Prague for its soldiers stationed in Pilsen, I volunteered to accompany them as an interpreter.

Like everything else, it was fun at first and then it became a bore. To drag twenty gum-chewing Yanks, Saturday after Saturday, to churches from four to eight, or to cafés from eight to midnight—those were our shifts—and to listen to the same old stuff: Say, ain't you people never heard of Coke machines? Hey, get a loada this church! Simply gorgeous! Oh yeah, gorgeous! And those same old questions, like a phonograph stuck in a groove: Say, don't you mind you've got them Ruskies over here? Hey, what the hell are you, anyway—a communist or a democrat?

Believe me, I heard enough of that kind of stuff in my department, where even pretty girls were possessed by politics and anybody who didn't belong to some party was fair game for proselytizing. They even wrestled for you in a literal sense of the word—Šiska the Social Democrat actually tore my jacket trying to yank me out of the grasp of a certain Populist. As for me—well, I was simply at a loss what to think about it all, in other words it was all too confusing. And so I joined the Gramophone Club.

In short, ladies, as you've no doubt gathered, I was an idealistic simpleton and I should have known quite clearly what to join and what to think. Or at least, I should have kept saying aloud that I think it.

But I'm an idiot.

I was born that way, and I'll stay that way.

It's incurable.

Even nowadays, although I've knocked around the world a bit and learned how to make the right faces and the right sounds, sometimes I still get so mad that I feel like screaming: Leave me alone! I haven't got any political convictions! I am nothing, I think nothing, I don't know—honestly, I simply don't know who is right and what's what! Yes, if you insist, I can declare unambiguously that you are right, but as far as my private opinion is concerned, I simply don't know. I don't know, and that's that! Leave me alone! I do my work, I blow my tenor sax night after night as well as I know how, just like that fellow over there, Bull Mácha, spends his days running a lathe to make an honest living. Why did you kick him out of the Bulvárka for dancing "in a provocative way," when there is no such a law? Why don't you let him wear his ducktail and walk on three-inch platforms if that's what gives him pleasure, him and his chick who also does an honest day's work, in the *Rudé Právo* canteen, of all places.

Never mind, excuse my nerves. They get the best of me every now and then. Let me return to my theme: those Yanks gave me a pain in the ass, with all their questions.

Pardon me.

I should use three dots, like Krpata.

Every Monday we used to play for the Yanks in the Bulvárka, though in those days it was called Alfa, if you remember. Those Monday evenings were meant to give them a proper send-off before they returned to their bases.

That's when I made my fateful blunder.

It was like this: the Yanks had just finished an infantile folk dance, we blew a few notes for them from sheet music they had brought with them, and they returned to their tables, all heated up. We took a break, I got up, and then I spotted one soldier, his name was Bob or Seymour or something like that, and this soldier—who was a real political nut—was motioning at me to come over. He was beckoning so insistently that I willy-nilly set out for his table—but when I saw who was sitting there with him I dropped the nilly and became all willy.

You see, it was a woman!

But what a woman!

Like an ad for Max Factor makeup and a Maidenform brassiere.

A joy to behold!

Bob-or-Seymour introduced me right away and the Yankee enchantress trilled a hawaya in a honeyed alto voice, her teeth pearling, her dimples dimpling, her Scarlett O'Hara pupils zeroing in on me—in short, I've never belonged among the nonflammables but at that moment I'd have caught fire had I been made of asbestos.

I stopped perceiving my surroundings and like a sentimental ninny I perceived nothing but her. Her name was Eileen. And she was such a joy.

A joy like . . . well, forget comparisons.

Zetka and the band launched into a boogie-woogie and instead of playing my tenor sax I sat next to Eileen and couldn't pry myself away.

In a daze, I asked her for a dance.

I'm sorry, I don't dance. Excuse me, she said, and it sounded like a Mellophone or another such instrument with an equally melodious name.

And so we just sat there and chatted.

God knows what about. I believe we talked about music, about jazz, symphonies, operas, which she said she adored. I have the impression we also talked about the Bird and the Duke but also about Aaron Copland, Darius Milhaud,

Frederick Delius and I praised them all because she adored
them, although I would have been hard-pressed if I had to
spell some of those names.

I'm not going into long descriptions, but it must be so
clear to you ladies that it was love at first sight and thus the
best thing that can happen to a human being on this earth.

Because nothing else in the world is worth a shit.

Pardon me.

But there you have another axiom, ladies.

I floated on clouds of enchantment and felt blissful; I
don't think I had felt that blissful before, except perhaps
with Geraldine, but that's another story. This was different,
a sweet promise, a marshmallow that wasn't going to cloy or
melt away or turn gooey.

And then . . .

I had already written Zetka off that evening. When Lexa
came to fetch me I told him to let Zetka know that I was
through for the night and that they should manage with
three saxophones. Lexa interpreted that to mean that I was
struck by an attack of cardiac intoxication. And the band
played for us a jazzed-up version of "Love, Sweet Love."

Ah, yes. In those days the band still had a sense of humor,
they pulled real jokes, not just phony gags to amuse the public. Later, Harry and Lexa got locked up for trying to cross
the border, and that was the end of the band and of the jokes.

I tried a few more times to lure Eileen onto the dance
floor, but each time she gave me a warm smile and said: No
thank you, I really don't dance. And then: Please stop asking
me. I've already told you, I don't dance. And when at last her
face shrank into an angry grimace with two wrinkles at the

root of her nose, I stammered: Excuse me, excuse me, please!

Bob-or-Seymour seemed to have evaporated or changed his form or dissolved in alcohol, in a stein of beer I guess, because that was the only kind of alcohol served in the joint.

Truly, I had no idea what happened to him.

And don't get the notion that I had only dreamed him up. When I first entered the place, he was really there and he really spoke to me.

And then he simply vanished.

It's a fact.

And all of a sudden, while the band was on a break, the smooth Yankee cooing of endearing words that seemed to flow effortlessly from my lips was interrupted by a racket from the outside.

Eileen turned her profile to me, the gilded letters "U.S." on the lapels of her uniform glistened, the red heart hanging from a multicolored ribbon took on a ruby sheen.

And fool that I was, I took it for some sort of jewelry!

On a uniform!

My only excuse was the fact that in addition to my normal, natural idiocy, love had made me into an even bigger fool.

Look, Eileen said. I turned to the window. Out in the street I saw a procession, a sea of red banners and portraits of Stalin of the kind painted by artistically gifted schoolchildren who have a progressive-minded teacher.

How can you stand it? Eileen asked. I felt as if I had been stabbed. Again, politics. And this morning star, this Venus, this new constellation had to bring up politics!

Stand what? I said.

Don't you people have any national pride? she said. How can you walk around carrying flags of a foreign country? Your own flag is completely lost among them, if it's there at all, she said, watching the procession.

Eileen, please, can't we drop the subject?

But this interests me, she said with determination, and two wrinkles formed above her nose. That upset me. OK, I said.

It interests me. I can't understand it. She spoke in that twangy American English of hers, which would probably give a British aristocrat heart failure but which made my native language seem like the speech of peasants. In such situations, a foreign language always has that kind of effect.

I said to Eileen: National pride has nothing to do with it. It's a matter of gratitude.

I perpetrated one of the truths.

Eileen's eyes opened wide: Gratitude?

Yeah, I said. The Russians liberated us, and we're grateful.

But that's silly, Eileen answered. We were attacked just like they were, except it was the Japanese, and so we went to war, too. Why don't you carry American flags? Or British? Or French?

We do.

Where? Where are they? Look! Not a single one.

I looked, but of course quite unnecessarily. In a procession of this sort they obviously weren't going to wave any stars and stripes.

Eileen lectured me: The war was won by the Allies. Some of them cleaned out one country, others another. That depended on the strategic and tactical situation and geographic location. She spoke like a handbook for officer cadets. So if you must show gratitude, you should carry flags of the U.N.

Oh, please, can't we drop this subject? Let's dance!

She blanched a little, those two wrinkles reappeared over her nose. Don't you understand English? I do not dance! She seemed rather irritated.

Pardon me, I said quickly.

She kept on insisting: Answer me! She leaned her elbows on the table. On a finger of her alabaster hand there was an aquamarine ring. She was probably no rich American, certainly not, otherwise she wouldn't be a WAC corporal. But she was a beautiful American.

Fragrant as coconut milk.

Why are you doing things like that? Why are you doing it? I know the standard answer, but what is the real reason?

What do you mean? I pretended not to understand.

Those Russian flags. Why do you have all those Russian flags all over the place?

Instead of saying what I truly thought, I uttered a truth.

Perhaps it was because I had been hearing it everywhere, or perhaps because I liked to tease Americans with Bolshevik slogans when they got on my nerves.

I uttered a truth. And I uttered it in the proper classical *pluralis majestaticus.*

Listen, I said. I know that other nations were involved in the war besides Russia. But people simply feel the greatest gratitude to those who have shed the most blood for them. And that was the Russians. Yes, we know that America deserves credit for victory, we don't deny it. But America gave material aid, tanks, planes, ships, whereas the Russians gave their blood.

That's as far as I got. I suddenly noticed that Eileen was no longer sitting, but standing. The Russians gave blood, she said, and her voice was trembling. The Russians gave blood and the Americans tanks. You . . . you . . . you stupid bastard! she said, all excited. The Russians blood and Americans guns, she said, the red heart trembling on her chest, and all of a sudden there was an explosion in front of my eyes, stars streamed around my head and I saw Lexa choking on the podium right in the middle of a solo.

I shook my head and realized I'd been slapped.

Amid the falling stars I saw Eileen indignantly walking away.

I watched her saucily short, reddish hair under her cap, the smooth, neatly fitting back of her uniform, the curve of her slender behind, the legs . . .

Yes, dear Lord, you'll probably never forgive me, and even if you do, old softie that you are, I'll still keep kicking myself for the rest of my life.

Here I'd been dishing up one truth after another, like a candidate for public office, and it turned out that she simply couldn't dance with me. Only an acrobat could dance with that kind of prosthesis for a leg.

Since that time I can't bear truths.

I know, maybe a truth becomes Truth only *en gros. En détail* it's at most a *lèse majesté.* But still, it gives me a pain in the . . . , to use the three-letter word so favored by Krpata.

Pardon me, ladies.

Don't think me rude.

There's nothing in the world ruder than truths.

a case for
political inspectors

We believe in man, in his infinite
capacity for development.

Dalibor Pechácek,
Of Class Consciousness

T HERE are various reasons why people become
"progressive."
Some do it out of hunger and misery.
Others, out of intellectual convictions.
Some do it for the sake of careers.
And some, because they shit in their pants.
The latter was the reason our good Judge Bohadlo progressed in such a progressive fashion, may the Good Lord
bless his soul.
Actually, this is one more story about Political Inspectors,
individuals entrusted with guarding socialist values and check-
ing people's political correctness. It is a story about watchful-
ness and vigilance. And though no PI's appear here directly,
they hover in the background and are present in spirit.

When I first had the honor of meeting Judge Bohadlo, he turned out to be a well-preserved, elderly gentleman. A kindly looking chubby fellow, with delicate, rosy cheeks that bespoke fine meals and choice wines, delicate rosy hands that had never known manual labor, a round little belly and a mouth shining like Klondike gold.

A flat in a modern apartment house, a spouse bedecked with bracelets, an aristocratic little dog—as solid a couple as a Biedermeier chair or a table at the Hotel Ambassador.

A district judge or something of the sort, I didn't know his exact title but certainly a few ranks above the ordinary. His schoolmate was the father of my former girlfriend Julie Nedochodil, and it was at the Nedochodils that I had the honor.

In precommunist days, he used to visit there once in a while, when he had some business to discuss with Papa Nedochodil. After 1945, he formed some sort of connection with cloisters, church organizations and the Catholic Populist party.

He had already been involved in politics before the war, but in those days he was connected with the Agrarian party.

After discussions in Papa Nedochodil's study, Madam Nedochodil would invite them to the dining room for a bit of refreshment, and there they sat, sipped wine from South-Moravian cloisters and munched on sandwiches spread with goat cheese from East-Slovakian cloisters, while Judge Bohadlo recounted tales from the good old golden days.

He especially liked to recall the fox hunts on the estates of Prince Schwarzenberg and Baron Simmenthal. But his dearest friend was Count Humprecht Gelenj, who entered the Premonstration Order in 1945.

The judge made no secret of his distaste for communism.

And so they lived, grew obese and enjoyed themselves.

In February 1948, the ground under Judge Bohadlo's feet suddenly gave way, but he grasped the support held out to him and performed a grandiose somersault.

He applied for membership in the Communist party.

And what's more—he was accepted.

And so Judge Bohadlo became a communist.

Naturally, this triggered difficult inner struggles.

Seeking relief for his spiritual torments, he turned to Papa Nedochodil for moral support.

He tried to justify himself:

First of all, he is unused to physical work. Suppose they fired them, what then?

Secondly, he supports a sick wife, who needs spa treatments.

And thirdly, somebody's got to stick it out, to save what can be saved.

This third, heroic sounding argument met with Papa Nedochodil's half-hearted approval.

But the big blow was still to come. The pope issued an excommunication decree.

And he really let them have it.

Excommunication applied to all members of the Communist party, as well as any person aiding the communist movement directly or indirectly (reading communist books and newspapers, listening to communist broadcasts, etc., etc.).

In other words, in Czechoslovakia, it applied to practically everybody.

Above all, of course, to Party members.

For a long time, Judge Bohadlo failed to come to Papa Nedochodil's house. Then one day he appeared. His pink second chin dropped lifelessly, his pince-nez kept dropping off his nose.

Somebody, he said in a shaky voice, has to stick it out, save what can be saved. As long as he remains in inner opposition.

Papa Nedochodil had a rather different opinion and his gaze upon the judge's pale pink cheeks was somewhat disdainful, yet because he was basically a kindly soul he offered his friend such an ingenious construction of *reservatio mentale* as applied to the papal decree that the judge began to see that ominous document in an entirely new light. He gobbled up the roast pork Madam Nedochodil offered him, washed it down with mead, and left in a virtually buoyant mood.

All the same, an evil deed is an evil deed. One can keep on thinking up excuses and seek relief in dialectic logic, but an evil deed gives rise to a bad conscience, and that works night and day.

With a sledgehammer.

Two days later, we had the judge back on our neck. Full of torment, near collapse. Somebody, he whispered, has to stick it out . . .

A new injection of casuistry, combined with almond pastry and mead, put him back on his feet.

He left in much calmer shape.

Two days later, he returned.

Very shaken.

And so it continued, until the mead ran out.

He stopped coming for a long time.

And then one day he suddenly appeared at the door, looking radiant. He announced that he had consulted a confessor.

The confessor had reassured him: Somebody indeed has to stick it out and save what can be saved.

I was rather surprised, but then I discussed the matter with Julie in her room, and that clever girl reconstructed the story this way: Imagine, she said, a clergyman who is in every respect a proper priest, except that the poor fellow lacks the courage of the early Christian martyrs. It's hard to condemn him for that, even in this nation of Hussite heroes. And now somebody walks into his confessional, kneels down and confesses that he sinned by joining the Communist party. What is that poor old fellow to do?

Of course, the matter is clear, according to the papal decree he is forbidden to absolve him as long as he remains in league with the godless brood.

Only . . .

Suppose the penitent is an undercover agent? If I refuse him absolution he may turn me in.

So imagine the situation: the judge is kneeling in the confessional, trembling, gnawed by his bad conscience.

Behind the grating sits the priest, trembling, the ugly thought of prison oppressing his mind.

This mutual trembling, naturally, could only be ended through compromise.

Thesis approved: Somebody's got to stick it out, save what can be saved.

Proviso: The aforementioned somebody must not perform anything evil, and in his heart must continue to oppose those communist ideas that conflict with the teachings of the church.

Please note: "those communist ideas that conflict with the teachings of the church." In other words, not communism as such.

Why not?

Well, because the reverend father was suddenly struck by still another terrible possibility: if that penitent is an informer, he could just as well turn him in for giving absolution as for refusing to give it. After all, what would it mean to absolve someone of communism? That would logically imply that the reverend father considered communism a sin, and that he was guided by the pope rather than by the State Bureau for Religious Affairs.

In short, that poor priest spent some very trying moments in connection with Judge Bohadlo's confession.

The compromise lay uneasy on his conscience, and so he at least urged the penitent to practice energetically the virtue of Christian charity: concretely, in terms of the judge's profession, he should do his utmost to ease the human lot of the prisoners with whom he came in contact.

This was a program to which Judge Bohadlo responded with the greatest of enthusiasm.

He repeatedly reported to us on his acts of charity:

He smuggled chocolate bars to Miss Skladanovská, daughter of the former senator and friend of my former love Julie Nedochodil, whom he had socked with two years in jail for an attempt at illegal emigration.

He frequently smuggled packages of American vitamins into the cell of Mr. Simms, a former editor whom he had slammed with a fifteen-year sentence.

After meting out a life sentence to a certain wholesale merchant, the judge patted him on the back and whispered in his ear: Keep up your spirits, friend!

Whereupon that malcontent answered in a loud voice: Shut your trap, you swine!

Ingratitude rules the world. Dr. Bohadlo performed his good deeds without thought of reward, like a true scout.

He would recount these stories to us, always managing to add his denunciation of communist legal and investigative methods, and he let us in on some unbelievably sensational details of political trials.

A bad conscience turned the judge into an ideal source of juicy information.

The Voice of America would have paid me for them in gold.

But I have always followed the principle: freedom is better than riches.

And it's paid off for me so far.

The judge kept cursing communism like the prophet Habakuk, for reasons best known to himself, while furiously munching on hors d'oeuvres and pastry. His eyes burned with indignation. In those moments his conscience grew calmer. But then he'd leave for a street rally or the meeting of some organization where he'd excoriate the imperialists, and his bad conscience stuck out its horns.

At Papa Nedochodil's, of course, he tried as hard as he could to ridicule such proceedings. After indoctrination

sessions where they discussed dialectical and historical materialism, he declared (at Papa Nedochodil's): I've forgotten
more of this nonsense than they will ever learn. I recognized
it for trash when I was still a young puppy like you, he
added, turning to me.

He said it in the heat of the moment, so I didn't take of-
fense. I understood him.

But that didn't help.

They promoted him.

His wife won approval for sojourn in a spa, whereas the
wife of an impoverished shoemaker in the judge's basement,
who stubbornly insisted on remaining a private entrepre-
neur, was rejected.

Does that surprise you? You don't seem to understand:
Judge Bohadlo was politically sound. A working member of
the intelligentsia.

Whereas the shoemaker? Suppose they gave him a bit of
leeway. In no time at all, he'd hire apprentices and start ex-
ploiting the working class. People of his type are incorrigible. Petty entrepreneurs are the germs of capitalism.

Judge Bohadlo thus became an ever higher jurist and in
the end an instructor of political education.

He stuck it out, that's true, and saved what could be saved.

In the single year of 1950 he smuggled in 28 packages of
American chocolate, 5 kilos of vitamins, 3 kilos of sugar,
2,000 cigarettes, 18 books for reading and 22 prayer books.

He kept precise records, including name, date, type of
merchandise and quantity.

In excoriating the Communist party he reached a Mc-
Carthyite level of intensity.

And so it continued.

What's that?

You're asking whether he's still a high judge? Whether they ever unmasked him and got rid of him?

But my dears, you are so naive!

Of course, obviously, naturally. In the end, our society always gets rid of its internal enemies, even if they managed to lead it by the nose for years. Our society has eliminated—and continues to eliminate—all parasites who believe they can hide behind slogans and phrases and conceal their foul schemes.

Judge Bohadlo?

Of course our society got rid of him in the end.

How?

He died.

A stroke.

Say what you like, death is still the best Political Inspector.

how they got nabbed

Everything that happens, happens by necessity.

Democritus

HEAR they let Hiram C. Nutsbellow out, on account of good behavior. OK, I really have nothing against it. I've never had anything against Hiram C. Nutsbellow. But are they going to let Licátko out, too? That's what I'd really like to know. Because I'll bet Licátko is on his best behavior. He has never been anything but a well-behaved, quiet, inconspicuous hipster, the kind you see on Saturday nights puking at street corners of downtown Prague.

I have this feeling that although Nutsbellow might be out, Licátko shouldn't hold his breath. Sure, he's been in longer than Nutsbellow, but Nutsbellow is a Somebody. I mean Nutsbellow is like hard currency, a valuable item of trade. And Licátko? Few people know that he even exists.

Maybe Sylvie still does. Then again, maybe even she no longer cares.

Actually, when I think about it, I've never had much to do with Licátko. He was a very close-mouthed hipster.

Now, take Paul Rameš, his mouth never took a rest. He was a born announcer and commentator. He won't be coming out so very soon. I just can't imagine him behaving good.

It's all a matter of character. Rameš was a vibes player and most vibes players have been born on a funny farm. Paul Rameš certainly was a nut. At one time he played with us in Krinolin, that was when vibes came back into style and before they put the kabosh on bebop. He was never a wheeler-dealer, he just tried to make a little extra because he had a wife and a kid whom he drowned in puppy love. Not that the fat treasure of his deserved it, candy and loafing had turned her into a horizontal giant, she wasted whole days glued to a park bench or gobbling it up with her hen friends at the Myšák Coffee House. Well, Paul was simply a nut.

During the day he worked for News Limited, the outfit that later became so notorious. He was terribly happy there. When he heard that I was thrown out of Anglo-American Studies because I was under suspicion of believing in God, he tried to talk me into joining up with them. You jerk, he used to say, staring at me with his crossed eyes, five thou for five hours a day, as much chewing gum as you can stuff in your mouth and now and again some used but great-looking threads from Nutsbellow—and besides, from time to time there is a chance for a bit of unofficial business, if you know what I mean—he would add, winking with his crossed eyes and grinning like a moron, the way he did when pounding the vibes. Screw Zetka. Two or three sessions a week with them should be enough to keep you solvent. He showed me a dirty, well-worn shirt inherited from Nutsbellow, and gave me a package of gum. Come and join us, you jerk, the boss asked me to keep on the lookout for a good man.

And so I went to look the joint over. They had their offices in Kabert Street. Leather club chairs, pinup girls and incredibly endowed strippers on the walls, quiet as a churchyard except for the back room, where teletypes gently clicked while a leather-clad hipster sipped a glass of whiskey, feet propped on desk and syphon in hand.

Licátko.

We barely exchanged three words of greeting, something like hi . . . hi . . . ahoy, and then I glanced at the beat-up teletype. A tape was just sliding out of it.

Paul picked it up, and his crossed eyes twinkled with amusement. I glanced over his shoulder and saw the word MINDZENTI. And words like FRAMEUP and COMMUNIST TRIAL.

You've got it pretty nice here, I said, looking around. I noticed that the hipster was quietly giving me the once-over.

And what fun! Paul said. You wanna see how we get our kicks?

Sure, I answered.

All right, watch this! Paul sat at the teletype, thought for a moment and then reached into the keyboard. I read over his shoulder:

(PRAGUE) TERROR IN THE STREETS. A MAN JUMPED OUT OF A TROLLEY CAR ON WENCESLAS SQUARE JUST AS IT WAS TURNING THE CORNER AT THE NATIONAL MUSEUM. AT THAT MOMENT TWO MEN CARRYING AN ENORMOUS PORTRAIT OF STALIN PASSED THE CAR

AND THE UNFORTUNATE TRAVELER FLEW THROUGH
THE PAINTING LEAVING A BIG HOLE BETWEEN THE
RUSSIAN DICTATOR'S EYES. THE MAN WAS SEIZED ON
THE SPOT BY TWO HEAVILY ARMED POLICEMEN,
CRUELLY BEATEN, HURLED UNCONSCIOUS INTO A
PATROL WAGON AND DRIVEN AWAY. NOTHING IS
KNOWN ABOUT HIS FURTHER FATE.

As Paul finished typing and the tape vanished into the
machine, to reappear somewhere among our foreign enemies, Licátko burst into laughter.

That's great, I said.

And backed out of there as quickly as I could.

I suppose this world needs a few idealists. But I've never
counted myself as one of them.

Then official lightning struck several times in rapid succession as far as jazz and bebop were concerned, and some
drunk sat down on top of Paul's vibes. We barely managed to
scrape up a few gigs in the few joints left for the non-builders
of socialism. I lost track of Paul. He did meet me a couple of
times and tried to talk me into joining up with Nutsbellow;
he enticed me with trousers made over from American officers' pinks, cartons of Chesterfields and a pornographic magazine with stereoscopic glasses that made the pictures burst
right out of the page. But I was wary and chose to pretend
that I was lazy and liked to sleep during the day.

Then Rameš disappeared completely. Instead, I bumped
into Licátko, under rather remarkable circumstances.

One Thursday, when our usual joints were closed, the
band made an outing to Sázava, to the summer place of a cat

named Davida. Spring was just starting to tune up, the village looked like a ghost town, everything still locked up and boarded up, and just about the only thing that moved were patches of fog rolling over the water.

And suddenly, who trots out of the neighboring cottage if not Licátko, in gardening pants with white stitching and cotton suspenders like they wear in the States, and right behind him who comes hopping out into the fresh air but a blonde looker, a blonde so gorgeous that our eyes turned downright astigmatic.

Behind me Davida whistled through his teeth.

Licátko smiled shyly and said hi.

The looker realized that she was in deshabille and withdrew.

We, too, went inside and Davida sat down on his bunk.

Gentlemen, he said, this beats Sodom!

What do you mean? You know those cats? I asked.

You bet! said Davida. That's Licátko of Licátko and Co., bathroom accessories. And that relic of bourgeois taste is his mother.

So what? said Ríša. He is spending the weekend with his mother, that's all.

And that indeed turned out to be the case. That night, we lay on our bunks, the room dark except for the glow of cigarettes as Davida explained Licátko's history. Our neighbors' windows were lit up and we could hear the sounds of Glen Miller and Stan Kenton. This, in brief, was the story:

Licátko's old man owned a factory manufacturing bathtubs and bidets. He married a Russian émigré who bestowed on him Licátko Junior. At the time of the communist takeover she died of a stroke. A couple of months ago dad married again and the rosebud presently being entertained by Kenton's mellow tones was the bathtub king's second wife. She was two years Licátko Junior's junior.

Davida fell silent. Then he got up, and gazed for a long time at the windows of the neighboring cottage, their brightness now dimmed by shades.

By sheer coincidence, I kept running into them. The very next Sunday we met at the races, and Licátko introduced his stepmother to me. Her name was Sylvie. Close up, after talking to her a bit, she didn't have that dynamic impact, but in a way that was to her advantage. She came across as a quiet, nice kid, as sweet on the eyes as a sunset in the Tatras and as pleasing on the ear as the sounds of a glass harmonica when you're resting in an easy chair at a resort hotel after a first-rate dinner.

A veritable music of the spheres.

And she was tailor-made for Licátko. Silent, unassuming, clean, neat. An American type.

She had a perfect class background: she came from a proletarian family, and was an orphan to boot. She didn't have much schooling, started working as a salesgirl at the White Swan, but the pay was so miserable that she switched to a factory job.

The factory turned out to be Licátko and Co., enameled bathroom fixtures.

One day, the owner of the factory saw her enameling a bidet, and started to smolder.

Soon he caught fire.

He was the one that turned her into an American looker. But when you got to know her personally, she remained nice and unassuming and proletarian. I mean that as words of praise.

But I'd better not think about it too much.

That day at the races I began to sense what Licátko was all about, and at the same time the signal of an unpleasant premonition began blinking in my head.

Licátko bet stubbornly all afternoon. He circled the bookmakers' booths like a hawk around sparrows, he kept making notes, counting, figuring. By the time the horses stopped running he was ahead by a hundred crowns. He bought Sylvie a bouquet of tulips and a bunch of radishes.

And so it went, Sunday after Sunday. And then? Well, it ended the way it had to end, the way everything ends.

Badly.

Licátko had practically turned into the phantom of the turf. He haunted the first floor at Juliš where they bet on foreign races. In the summer he spent every Sunday in Karlsbad, in the spring and fall at the Chuchle track. Always with notebook and pencil in hand, taciturn, eyebrows knitted in concentration, Sylvie, elegant and vivacious, always beside him.

They were such a classical hipster pair, the very Platonic idea of hipsterdom, that I was ready to bawl with sheer happiness every time I saw them.

A joy forever, as Keats would say.

Except that Licátko went broke, started pawning his overcoats and other objects, and after a while there was nothing left in his flat except pawn tickets.

He thought of trying his hand at translating. In those days there was still a shortage of people who could read Cyrillic texts, and so Licátko, who inherited some Russian from his mother, offered his services.

They were accepted, and Licátko was given *The Victory of Collective Farmer Vadim* for translation.

For a time, Paul filled in for him at the News Limited teletype desk, and Licátko translated the collective farmer's progressive opinions. But it was no use. In no time at all he squandered his advance and the track kept gobbling up one pawn ticket after another.

He pawned Nutsbellow's Underwood.

"You crazy? What in the world are you gonna tell him?" I said, when we accidentally happened to meet in the pawnshop.

He smiled sheepishly and shrugged his shoulders.

They gave him quite a decent sum for the Underwood and he was off to Juliš.

By the sunset the sum was gone.

Soon thereafter everything caved in on him, like a rain of left and right hooks on a punch-drunk boxer.

At home, his dad found out about his affair with Sylvie.

Nutsbellow discovered that his Underwood, wall clock and oil painting of President Truman were in hock. With a shy smile, Licátko offered him the pawn tickets.

In front of his dad, too, Licátko appeared genuinely contrite, but that didn't stop the former factory owner from giving Junior a few hefty smacks.

On Sylvie her husband made use of a bullwhip.

She cried, and Licátko was incensed. Miraculously, he

found himself a small flat and moved out of the family house. Sylvie moved in with him, but Licátko Senior refused a divorce and so they lived in sin.

Actually, that was hard to believe, because they both looked so innocent.

Hiram C. Nutsbellow behaved like a true gentleman, or at least so it seemed to me at the time. He redeemed the pawned items himself and even gave Licátko a raise.

I thought—jerk that I was—that it was on account of his social consciousness. On account of Sylvie and so on.

I was simply a jerk. A triple-crowned idiot.

Licátko gradually got his belongings out of hock and started furnishing a home. First he redeemed his silver cocktail shaker, then his tuxedo, an ivory mahjong set, and a Chinese screen with somewhat juicy depictions (which they had at first rejected on the grounds that socialist pawnshops do not accept pornography, but then relented on account of its quality material). All these things were now safely back in the apartment, along with Sylvie in toreador pants ensconced in the kitchen corner. She had quit the bidet factory as soon as she became Madam Licátko, and after her husband had slammed the door on her she had to look for other work.

This time it was easier. She worked at what she was born for. She became a fashion model.

Now she hopped about happily in the kitchen nook, draped in a pink apron with the inscription KISS ME, HUBBIE!, while in another corner Licátko pounded the typewriter.

When I think of that blissful domestic scene I could bawl like a whore.

The relationship that developed between Licátko and me was kind of strange. Maybe it was because I continued to have this inkling that the whole thing was destined for a rotten end. I don't know why, I simply had that feeling. Whenever I saw them living like two lovebirds from an ad in *Ladies Home Journal* I felt a pang of the blues and waited for new troubles.

And I was right.

But before the disaster I met once more with Paul Rameš. That very same day that *The Victory of Collective Farmer Vadim* came out, the book that Licátko translated and that paid for their new vacuum cleaner.

I ran into Paul under the Libeň viaduct. He was wearing a bricklayer's shirt and overalls, and I was afraid he'd gotten fired from his cushy job. No way, he reassured me, News Limited is beyond the reach of Political Inspectors. He was still with them, working there till noon and then moonlighting on a construction job in the afternoon. Just like the USA. The pay in the office is small, there are few gigs for vibes players, and bricklayers make good money.

But we're doing OK, he explained, zeroing his crossed eyes into the distance behind me. Nutsbellow drops a gift parcel our way now and again, recently I got a suit, a bit used but made of Harris tweed, occasionally a few cartons of Chesterfield land on my desk, but that's the one thing Nutsbellow is pretty stringent about, he doesn't want to tangle with people's democratic laws.

Natch, said Paul. You bet, I answered.

Why don't you come up with me to the house, he said. You haven't been to see us since the flood.

So I went with him.

At the house sat the horizontal Mrs. Paul, devouring a larger-than-life chocolate rabbit, an item either imported or meant only for export. This one came wrapped in fancy green foil, too fancy for our circumstances. The child named Ellen was playing with a velvet monkey, and who sat there in a leather jacket if not Licátko! Next to him sat another cool cat looking like a hit man from a gangster movie, with a jacket to match.

They stood up when we entered.

This is Bubeník, the murderer, said Licátko with a shy smile.

The cool cat grinned under his mustache. Mrs. Rameš wagged her finger at Licátko. Paul Rameš burst into laughter.

Hi, I said, shaking the cat's hand. I felt strange.

There followed some conversation about arranging the details. I gathered that whatever he was going to do, he would do it in the West.

Fine goings on, I thought to myself, may the Lord have mercy on us, and I turned to Mrs. Rameš, who offered me a bite of her chocolate rabbit.

Little Ellen had just torn the monkey's head off, licked the sawdust inside and started bawling.

Fortunately, it was getting late and I hurriedly made my farewells.

The cat in the jacket again rose politely to his feet, shook my hand and again grinned under his mustache.

I felt extremely uncomfortable.

Then, as usually happens in such cases, one two three, left hook, right hook, uppercut, KO.

The radio announces that they've picked up Hiram C. Nutsbellow.

I rush to Licátko's place. Sylvie in tears. They picked up Licátko.

As I gallop down the stairs, I pass two strange-looking guys with hats pulled down over their eyes.

I pause in the hallway, and sure enough: after a few moments, lots of crying. They nab Sylvie.

I jump in a taxi and I'm off for Kabert Street. I can't get poor Sylvie out of my mind, my head is spinning with crazy plans for helping her.

I get to Kabert Street just in time to see Paul Rameš being dragged to the paddy wagon, fighting all the way. They manage to shove him in. Terror in the street. Just the way he dreamed it up on the teletype message.

Let's get away from here, I tell the cabbie.

In the evening I stayed home, glued to the radio. Not a word over Radio Prague, but plenty from The Voice of America: "Prague," I made out the announcer's voice over the crackle of jamming. "The communist police today arrested the director of the News Limited press agency, Hiram C. Nutsbellow. Hiram C. Nutsbellow is being accused of espionage. Paul Rameš, an employee of the agency, sent us this afternoon the following teletype message: 'Today at two o'clock, director Nutsbellow and editor Licátko were dragged off by the police. This message is a warning to the Free World. No matter what happens, we shall remain firm, faithful to freedom and democracy.' Our attempts to establish contact with editor Paul Rameš have so far remained fruitless. It seems that his dire prediction came true. Dear listeners, join us to honor in our thoughts these heroes of democracy."

That's what they said.

You have to hand it to Rameš, he may have been a bit of a nut, but he had style.

Something of a hero.

Except that he chose the wrong side. It wasn't his fault. We can choose what we want, but as for wanting what we want . . . there's the rub, as Schopenhauer warned. Freedom of the will doesn't stretch quite that far.

And so they threw the book at them: class enemies, golden youth, scion of an industrialist corrupted by compulsive gambling, relations with the stepmother, sexual perversions—no, actually that was quite a different case, the case of the Mengele brothers—living beyond their means, parasites on society, individuals averse to honest work.

And then, the prosecutor: abetting espionage, supplying slanderous information about the socialist state for the use of enemy propaganda.

Also, giving aid and comfort to Bubeník, a spy and murderer.

The last item made me feel ill. Bubeník had hit some undercover cop over the head and made away with secret documents. They never found him.

A bad show. Sick at heart, I scanned the papers to see how they had dealt with Licátko and Sylvie.

They got the limit. They really gave them the works.

Hiram C. Nutsbellow, twenty-five years.

Paul Rameš, twenty.

Licátko, fifteen.

Sylvie, a year.

When they let her out, she looked just as good as ever, even better, in fact. But she came out with such sad eyes. Went to work in a factory. Tesla, the television outfit.

Licátko Senior, the former industrialist, divorced her while she was still behind bars. He got away with that, because Sylvie had committed a crime against the people's socialist democratic laws.

A few years have now passed, and nowadays Sylvie is once again working as a fashion model. That's good news. And yet, it's still so sad. You see, Sylvie remarried, a designer from the House of Fashion.

And Nutsbellow is out again, while Licátko is still behind bars.

I'll bet he is a model prisoner.

I'm not talking about Paul Rameš. I doubt he is on good behavior. He never was.

But it's different with Licátko.

Now that they swapped that CIA agent Nutsbellow for some bolshie spy, will they take pity on Licátko?

That's what I'd like to know.

Then again, perhaps it's better this way. What would Licátko do, after Sylvie's forgotten all about him? God, what would the poor guy do?

little mata hari
of prague

Society does not consist of the guilty and the
innocent, but of those who have been exposed,
and those who have not yet been exposed.

Insp. Bohuslav Vodička

I BECAME ACQUAINTED with Geraldine during a
party game called "mouth mail" that we were
playing at a party celebrating Peter's twentieth
birthday. It goes like this: those present sit down around a
table alternately by sex, and they pass a wooden matchstick
along from mouth to mouth without using their hands.
Every time the matchstick has done a turn of the table, a
little piece is broken off, so that it is finally just a tiny
splinter of a thing, progressing around the table from one
player to the next more or less with the aid of the tongue.
The one who swallows it or loses it or drops it is required to
do some unpleasant task. It can also be played for forfeits,
which then turns into a striptease, but unfortunately that
didn't happen at Peter's birthday party. It is an unhygienic
and interesting game and, unlike other games, has amused

everyone with whom I have had occasion to play it, without exception.

And that evening I was in an especially advantageous
position, because on my right I had Lizette, and on my left,
the girl they had introduced to me as Geraldine, with the
face of a first-class Prague ladybird, black hair and black
eyes, golden mussels clipped into her little earlobes, in her
décolletage a Venetian cameo on a sharp chain, and on her
bare arms a collection of gold antiques; her dress was of
black taffeta, she smelled of perfumes, and she had a nice
mouth, seemingly created for this particular game. And she
possessed all that at the age of sixteen and a half.

For me, the evening ended unpleasantly, because I got
drunk and barely made it back to where I was to meet the
rest of my unit, the Sixth Tank and Self-Propelled Artillery
Training Battalion Chorus, with which I had performed the
previous afternoon at the plant of the firm that was our
patron. I arrived at the Denis railway station a minute after
half past four in the morning, undoubtedly in the tow of a
guardian angel, who likes to use an alcoholic fog to guide a
person safely to his destination, albeit that person had sinned
the sin of intemperance and had lost all sense of time and
space.

The next day I found a Venetian cameo in the pocket of
my uniform jacket.

I tried to recall what had happened, but the only thing
that came to my mind were wisps of a few foggy recollections of the Braunšlégr's courtyard and of some indecencies
that I had been committing there against Geraldine, primarily with my hands, nothing more than that.

Fortunately, I had another trip to Prague that same week, under the pretext of a medical appointment at the military hospital. As soon as they sent me on my way from the hospital at Strešovice, I headed toward Lizette's. She was a little offended, describing to me in detail my behavior at the party, with a commentary of her own. Her husband Richard, who happened to be home on a six-day pass, because his unit hadn't yet begun to apply the new military regulations for locking soldiers up hermetically within training compounds, also had a commentary, but a different one. The girl called Geraldine was apparently Lizette's brother Pete's girl, according to Lizette. That evening, drunk, I had molested her. I was lucky that Pete had gotten drunk before me so that he never noticed. I had behaved abominably. Said Lizette. On the other hand, her husband said that it wasn't me who had molested the girl, but that she had molested me, because she is a well-known *maîtresse* from the Spořilov district, and Pete is a fool if he doesn't know it. Lizette said that Pete is no fool, and that's just the reason that he is going with Geraldine. To have some fun. And that she's actually not that bad, that it's mostly a lot of talk and gossip. Whereupon Richard declared that clumsy as he is with girls, he wouldn't need more than half an hour to be tête-à-tête etcetera with Geraldine, and Lizette brushed him off contemptuously, how come it took him a year with her, Lizette, and that she'd really like to know how he'd do it with Geraldine in half an hour. Richard replied that she, Lizette, might also be a *maîtresse*—he knew that Lizette would be flattered by that esoteric term—and that's why it took him such an inordinately long time with her; but a *maîtresse* of a different type, and that is how he is prepared to prove his contention in deed, if Lizette is so anxious to see it. And Lizette was furious at how anything so dirty could have occurred to him, considering that he is married, and married in a church at that. I never did find out if it was her Catholic upbringing or just female logic. It was probably a mixture of both.

And so I offered to do the experiment for Richard.

Lizette looked at me suspiciously.

Richard gave me all his support.

"Fine," declared Lizette. "You go there, and in exactly half an hour, I'll ring the bell."

The proof was to be my word of honor.

I went.

Geraldine's family occupied a large apartment on the fifth floor of an apartment building that had belonged to them; at the very top of the building was a little five-sided tower and that is where Geraldine had her own room. The situation was favorable; she opened the door and stared at me, but without much talk or embarrassment she let me in, remarking quickly that she was home alone. She was wearing a blue sweater, a gray skirt and her bare, delicately hairy legs ended in a pair of brown and yellow sandals. She sat down on the couch; above it hung a British Airways map of the world, with British Airways calendars on the walls, along with French reproductions of Victorian prints, and under a photograph of a cheery-looking man with a flower in his buttonhole, with a black mourning ribbon across the corner, was something that surprised me: an empty ammunition belt from a machine gun. And everywhere there were plants, vases, figurines, fashion magazines from London and Paris, and on the desk an ugly statuette of King Kong, loads of knickknacks and gewgaws, and some red roses on the coffee table, so that the tower room was filled with a sweet fragrance. That fragrance, and all those knickknacks, and black-eyed Geraldine with those gold mussels on her earlobes again—the entire seductive syndrome inspired me to such a degree that I exceeded the prescribed time by seven minutes, and precisely twenty-three minutes after having rung the bell at the door with the brass plate that read Jarmil Kolben, MD, I was lying on the couch with Geraldine, fulfilling the conditions of the experiment.

Lizette was two minutes early, and she rang insistently.

Geraldine got up, annoyed, pulled her skirt back down to her knees, straightened her hair, quickly repaired her lipstick and went to the door. When she left the room, I looked in the mirror and saw I had red smears around my mouth.

I left them there.

It was proof to support my word of honor.

Lizette came in, ran her eyes around the room, and when she saw the smears around my mouth, she blushed a little.

Then, outside, she bawled me out.

But Richard snickered triumphantly.

In essence, Lizette was pleased too. She was hungry for sensations about the girls she knew; she was just upset that I had been the one to prove it.

Because, married or not, she still felt she had proprietary rights to me.

And so that is how I came to know Geraldine fully, and later I succeeded in finding out her prehistory as well. Her father had been a patriotic dentist; he fixed teeth at the Presidential Palace and those of what was left of the Bohemian aristocracy, exclusively with gold. For that reason he had died an unnatural death during an interrogation at the notorious Gestapo institution that was commonly known as the Pečkárna during the war. He had imported Geraldine's mother before the war from Great Britain. Her name was Genevieve and she was employed by British Airways, an organization of extreme interest to the State Security Police. Through her father, Geraldine came from a family whose prominent member was the famous nineteenth-century Czech writer Alois Jirásek. Through her mother, she was descended from an uncertain family in Soho, noteworthy only for exceptional physical beauty, and as a result—as Geraldine herself told me with a seductive glance—for a large number of single mothers. Her own mother was rescued from the traditional fate in her seventh month as a result of steps taken by the British ambassador at the Presidential Palace in Prague. There were always some sort of diplomatic troubles surrounding Geraldine.

I visited her again at the closest opportunity, and not on any instructions from Lizette, but we were left alone only for a little while—which was enough—and then Pete rushed in, and Geraldine's mama served tea in the dining room; in the course of tea, in order to make an impression on the two ladies, I divulged a number of military secrets, which were especially devoured by Pete Braunšlégr, because the next month he was due to be drafted into military service.

Geraldine was all over him.

Unexpectedly, I was unable to make a date with her.

When Pete went to the bathroom and mama to the kitchen for some fresh tea, I kissed Geraldine, and it seemed to me that she was expecting it.

But she didn't want to make a date.

And then back to Pete, the way she had before.

That confused me.

Later on, of course, I understood, and recognized that for her, it was all as natural as talking and laughing.

She was just that way.

Hard to understand.

And so nothing came of it all, and about three months rolled by. I was no longer a prisoner of the Tank and Artillery Battalion, but an NCO of the highest rank; I harassed rookies and trips to Prague were no problem.

One Saturday when I showed up at Lizette's, horror, confusion and tears reigned.

They had arrested Pete.

They had come for him at his barracks, dragged him off his bunk, nabbed him with his suitcase and all, and drove him away. He was in jail pending interrogation in České Budejovice, and Geraldine had just left to go there.

I went over to Geraldine's. For the first time mama, with a long cigarette holder, disclosed herself to me. With contempt in her voice, she revealed that they had interrogated Geraldine three times already, but Geraldine had stood firm against those idiots from the secret police and hadn't breathed a word.

What she could have said, I didn't know.

And I didn't ask.

Madame had a strong, penetrating but pleasant voice,

and her language was the language of salons, with expressions of the industrial bourgeoisie. She voiced the conviction that no intelligent person could be a communist. I voiced my agreement.

"And would you believe, Doctor," said mama, awarding me the title that I had been prevented from achieving by the postcoup purges, "would you believe that a child like that, Doctor, she isn't seventeen yet, would you believe that they would follow a child like that around and try to get things out of her?"

"No, really?" I wondered.

"Really," said mama. "Such a vulgar fellow, he doesn't even speak Czech right," she said with her English accent, "asking about the people who come here, wanting to know what they talk about, and who it is who comes here, what do you say to that, Doctor?"

"Dreadful," I said.

"But Geraldine sent him packing; I didn't expect that of the girl myself."

"And why did they—" I started to ask.

"You know, British Airways. They've been interested in the local office for a long time, but they didn't liquidate it until a month ago. And people from British Airways used to come here, along with Professor Vašek of the Faculty of Electronics and various people from society—so they were curious, as you can well imagine."

"And where are you working now, Madame?" I said.

"At the Research Institute for Heavy Engineering," she said.

Oh no, I thought to myself.

After six months in jail, Pete was solemnly sentenced to two years of hard labor for undermining troop morale. He had praised American army rations and somebody ratted on him.

Geraldine was harassed about ten times.

Once I was too.

Except that the army is a school of manly virtues. Before they came for me, I was forewarned. First by my driver, who came running into the bowling alley and announced that the secret policeman from division was looking for me down at battalion, and did I want to send a quick message home. I set out for battalion without sending any message. On the way, I was similarly warned by the quartermaster sergeant from the commissary warehouse, three petty officers from battalion and finally by my squad commander, for whom I had been secretly writing reports to present at political schooling sessions.

They didn't want a whole lot from me.

How do I know Peter Braunšlégr and what do I know about his family.

I described all of them as good citizens devoted to the people's democratic regime, and Lizette as a good comrade and friend of Comrade Deputy Director Pitterman. At this point my interrogator interrupted me and asked whether Lizette was my friend as well. Yes, I admitted, but in a different way from Comrade Pitterman. I described Richard as a devoted Communist, and myself as a nonparty Marxist.

After that they didn't bother me anymore.

And after he had served two months, Pete was released as part of an amnesty.

But by the time I got out of the army, everything had changed with Geraldine. True, she sat around with us while Pete described his adventures with interrogation, she was with him morally maybe, and almost certainly, she gratified him erotically after he was set free. But emotionally she was fluttering after an entirely different butterfly—a young man who wore a conical coat with wooden pegs for buttons, a year and a half before that finally became the style in Czechoslovakia too. His name was Paul, he had spent his childhood during the war in neutral Switzerland, he wrote surrealistic prose about the girls he happened to be going with at the time, he was a student at the English high school, and in the end—together with another phony named Bernard, who supported himself by selling penicillin on the black market—they filched two thousand crowns from Geraldine's flat.

After the evening when Pete was released from the clink and came home on a pass, I didn't see Geraldine for a long time. Nor their apartment, full of old-fashioned furniture, with gold jewelry in all sorts of odd drawers that no one in the family had any idea of, so that whenever Lizette wanted to dress up, all she had to do was go over to Geraldine's and inconspicuously borrow something. Nor even that tower room with the British Airways calendars, the ammo belt and the horrendous statuette of King Kong on the desk. Nor mama enveloped in cigarette smoke, with her sarcastic talk about the secret police and communists. Nor even the gold-framed portrait of Master Alois Jirásek that hung in the dining room, with an inscription in faded ink in the master's own hand enjoining someone to *Be a good daughter to your nation!*—someone who couldn't have been Geraldine, first because the master had passed on long before any British ambassadors had called at the Presidential Palace, and second because nobody knows just exactly how it is with nationality in these cases.

When they let me out of the army, I returned to Zetka's jazz band, and I lived under conditions very much in keeping with the people's democracy; at a time when jazz was not encouraged by the powers that be, I hung around the Alfa Cafe, but the situation was gradually improving until Zuzka, our singer, began proclaiming that before the year was out, she would be singing Ella Fitzgerald's repertoire again.

But before the year was out, something else happened first.

Just as I had placed my saxophone in its stand and was getting ready to take a break, a pretty girl stepped up to the bandstand, dressed in a white dress in a floral-print material that you just don't see in Prague, with gold all over her body and with gold mussels on her earlobes.

Geraldine.

She was now over eighteen, and prettier.

We had arranged a date in a minute.

She arrived in a suit straight out of *Vogue* magazine, with a big bow of nylon lace on the front of her blouse, and she twittered on about this and that through until evening. She told me she attends French lessons at the Language Institute mornings, and afternoons she works on some lathe in some small factory that belongs to the People's Cooperative of Toymakers or something. They had turned down her application for the university.

"What do you mean, afternoons? Isn't it afternoon now?"

"It is, but our director is wild about me. Whenever he sees me, his eyes get misty," she said. "I told him I didn't feel well. He always lets me go when I tell him I don't feel well."

"Geraldine, you're a sight for sore eyes," I told her.

She laughed, and told me about mama, about the society people, now for the most part behind bars, about how she has nothing but contempt for people who have no ambitions, that she has ambitions to see the world and be well dressed and learn languages, that is why she works in a factory and her mama lets her keep what she earns to buy her clothes with.

"Damn," I said, looking at her nylon lace, "but you must earn quite a bit. Where did you buy that material?"

"It was a gift," she said and hurriedly changed the subject, asking whether I still see Lizette, and how she always liked Lizette and saw in her an ideal woman, but that Lizette had disappointed her. Lizette would like to live a very classy life, but in essence she is a proletarian, from the family of a locksmith, and she never will have class.

I started showing up with Geraldine in public. She was a good person to be seen with. She knew how to converse pleasantly. She never said no to anything.

Gradually I found out that the fabrics were obtained for her by a Miss Jeanne Fullbridge of the British embassy.

"You know how it is, mama has contacts, through the people who used to be at British Airways."

I deliberately asked no questions about her mama's contacts.

Why put myself in danger?

But at the Medical Students' Ball, I ran into that voluble lady, and was obliged by circumstances to have a dance with her. She carried on her old familiar talk about communists and the absurdity of communism.

"Are you still in heavy engineering, Madame?" I asked.

"Yes, I am," she replied with a laugh. "Isn't that something? So much for their hiring policy!" She was still laughing. "First they spent a year investigating me on account of British Airways, and then they place me in a research lab for heavy engineering! I have access to all the statistics, all the plans—"

"Is that a fact?" I said quickly.

"I know it's incredible," she said, strolling around with me in fox-trot rhythm.

I didn't get it either.

But I intentionally didn't ask any questions.

"And how is your dear mother, Madame?" I preferred asking after the grandmother.

I would meet with Geraldine at noontime in the Koruna automat, where I went for the rum pudding and Geraldine for coffee with whipped cream. That was the sole gastronomical peccadillo she allowed herself. She chattered merrily about her new dress and pumps, about people from the factory, about how people there do nothing but their own outside work, and how there isn't a single fink among them, and once when they tried to place a fink there, the personnel man didn't approve it.

"The personnel man is with the Communists, but he's a real sweetheart," said Geraldine.

In the meantime, the situation for jazz was improving, and Zetka was rehearsing a jazz revue which was aimed, under the pretext of the scientific-historical presentation of the development of the music of the black people of America, at serving the hungry fans of Prague a full portion of the wildest syncopated cocktail that we were capable of mixing.

We utilized all the tricks, which were still necessary, to bring the whole thing to the stage. Including the scholarly discourse of Dr. L.P. Lunda, who—to his own amusement and that of other initiates—deduced the origin of pentatonics from class conflicts in the kingdom of Benin. And including Robert Bulwer, a defector of American origin who was obliged to seek asylum in Czechoslovakia for political reasons, because he didn't want to go in the army. We labeled him a noble successor to Bunk Johnson, and printed his name in big letters on the posters, concealing the proclamation he had made to the Czechoslovak Press Agency in small print inside the program.

On the eve of the concert, Geraldine visited me in my flat.

"What does one wear to the concert? A long evening gown?" she asked. "Or a cocktail dress? Or is an afternoon dress enough?"

"Geraldine, you can come, say, in a bathing suit, you're entitled," I said gallantly, the way she loved it.

"No, seriously," she said, "I'm coming with Jeanne. So I've got to know." Her black eyes were glowing with enthusiasm, and mingling in the stuffy air of my studio flat, with the smell of the pork roast my landlady Mrs. Ledvinova was making in her kitchen next door, there was a breath of society, Britain and the West.

So I advised her to wear a cocktail dress.

Among the jazz audience that arrived in all the colors of the rainbow, fighting for tickets in front of the theater, she looked like a royal princess.

The dudes swarmed around her like ants around a drop of honey.

For two hours, we blew Dixieland and bebop. The applause that exploded after every number was nearly atomic. Foot stamping, whistling, screaming and yelling the like of which the hall had never experienced before.

After the concert, Geraldine introduced me to Miss Jeanne Fullbridge.

As soon as I set eyes on her, I made my farewells and vanished.

I wasn't interested in a closer acquaintance.

It's like I say, why put yourself in unnecessary danger?

And right I was.

The next morning the phone rang. Lizette. "Did you know they picked up Geraldine and her mother?"

"Come on!"

"No, really, read it in the morning paper."

I rushed down to the newsstand. Miss Jeanne Fullbridge had been expelled by the Government of the Republic on twenty-four hours' notice. With the aid of former employees of the British Airways Company, she had been carrying on industrial espionage, taking advantage of her diplomatic immunity.

In connection with her case, several arrests had been made.

I went over to Lizette's. So far she didn't know any more details. But within the next few days, a lot of things came out. They had also arrested the boy Paul, the one in the conical coat, and turned him loose in about a week. They picked up Professor Vašek of the Faculty of Electronics, and didn't turn him loose. A bunch of people fell into it, from society and elsewhere.

"Idiots," Lizette described them. "They used to hang around there out of snobbism, all excited because Geraldine's old lady was British. Serves them right."

"British from Soho."

"We're not all in English Studies like you," Lizette snapped.

"And why did they do it?" I asked Lizette.

"I don't know," she said. "Geraldine's old lady was a fool, and so was Geraldine."

I expected them to pick me up too, but nothing happened.

"Tell me, Lizette, do you think that Geraldine did spying?" I asked after a time.

"She was dumb enough to," said Lizette. "And her mama was too. She could have figured that they'd come after her. Heavy engineering indeed!"

"That's a fact," I said. "But for crying out loud, what could Geraldine have spied on?"

"Heaven knows," said Lizette. "That woman from the embassy turned her head with nylon and made an errand girl out of her. And now she ups and claims diplomatic immunity and leaves Geraldine to take the rap."

"What else could she do?" I said.

"You think she'd do something if she could?" said Lizette.

"You're right," I said. "Geraldine served her purpose, and now she's expendable."

And then, a week after her twentieth birthday, they gave Geraldine five years.

Her mama got twenty-five.

That didn't bother me too much.

But I did feel sorry for Geraldine.

the well-screened lizette

All animals are equal,
but some are more equal than others.

George Orwell

WHEN they sacked me, they didn't sack Lizette. She got a clean bill of health, even though she had never taken a single exam in six semesters at the university. She hadn't even taken a colloquium. They sacked me, although I had passed five semesters including all necessary exams. But I was an element suspected of sympathies for the West, because everyone knew I played in Zetka's swing band. And also, like a bloody fool, I showed up at the political screening session in colored socks. Fendrych, the cross-eyed Political Inspector with buck teeth, stared at them throughout the session, and every time he asked me an important question—such as "Are you descended from the working class, colleague?" or "Do you believe in God, colleague?"—his eyes threaded the answer out of my socks, as if he was deeply offended by these symbols of bourgeois decadence.

Needless to say, I didn't pass. This same Fendrych passed Lizette, who was under no suspicion of harboring questionable sympathies, and quite rightly so. There was only one thing in the whole world for which Lizette had strong sympathies: Lizette herself.

Obviously, I wasn't present at her evaluation, but I can imagine the scene quite easily: Fendrych stared, but not at socks or anything of the sort. No, I am sure that Lizette had put on her oldest blouse, which bore the marks of rough embraces and working-class ardor. I have no doubt that she stressed the proletarian occupation of her father as stagehand at the National Theater, though normally she referred to her dad as "being with" the National Theater. They didn't question her about his political opinions, because he was a member of the working class; Lizette was thus saved from the need of lying. If Fendrych was blinking at anything, it was Lizette's majestically swelling bosom, or her knees covered with darned working-class stockings, which Lizette skillfully exposed to view, knowing full well that they were worth a pair of positive political points. And so Fendrych passed that green-eyed snake in the grass.

And why not? He had been panting after her for two years and she never fully rejected him, because she never fully rejected anybody who might possibly be of use to her.

She thus stayed on the faculty. Many people declared that they would never understand to their dying day how this beautiful wide-eyed bit of fluff could ever have passed a course in Old Church Slavonic, not to mention pasting together a doctoral dissertation. And on the surface, it does seem incredible, because to this day Lizette isn't sure whether Masaryk is spelled with an "i" or a "y," but anybody with a drop of sense need only take one good gander at Lizette for everything to become crystal clear.

By now, at thirty, Lizette is still a knockout. In America she'd be photographed in Technicolor, posing for Maidenform lingerie.

Looks, plus a cunning as immense as her abysmal ignorance of elementary grammar, minus any consideration for others, minus the slightest trace of altruism, plus exemplary single-mindedness when it comes to her own person.

Take that business with Old Church Slavonic: Lizette showed up for examination at a time when Professor Marek did not expect her and, as she had ascertained in advance, he was alone in his office. With lowered eyelids she confessed that she didn't know a single word of OCS but that she desperately needed a certificate of proficiency in order to pass her political evaluation. Professor Marek intended to get furious, but then he looked at Lizette's bra, then higher into her green eyes. There, he drowned.

And he wrote out a certificate for her.

It cost her a few trips to Hřebenka, where Professor Marek lived with his wife and three children. During those trips she had to listen to his life story. During the last journey he confessed to her that he, too, was bored to tears by Old Church Slavonic, and he offered her safe passage in all exams up to the doctorate, in return for occasional sexual favors. But Lizette was sparing with this kind of merchandise, and since she no longer needed to worry about OCS, she went into reverse and backed out of the garage.

In similarly debonair fashion she conquered literature, Russian, Marxism, everything.

I happen to know, because Lizette had a soft spot for me in her heart, which mellowed to the tones of a tenor sax. That may seem like a violation of natural law, for a stone is a stone; I guess Lizette's heart was simply a special kind of stone. It happened when we played in Vlachovka. Her heart started beating in sync with my solos and after the concert I got to know her well, that green-eyed snake in the grass. Yes, she belonged among a special group of beautiful women, a group that's now dying out; Prague is becoming integrated. Lizette left in time, she slithered out of Prague all the way to Rio de Janeiro, God help her. But even if she were to slither all the way to the moon, in her heart she'd remain a snake in the grass.

As far as the doctorate goes—well, that was a bit more complicated. After carefully surveying the situation she chose psychology as her field of specialization, because she correctly pegged Professor Zajc as the most approachable of her teachers, from a strictly human point of view. She also set her sights on a certain classical philologist, a scholarly young woman whose knowledge in the field of Women's Studies was strictly theoretical. Lizette provided him with his first opportunity for practical, preliminary research. Her dissertation was finished within a quarter of a year and it was such an oustanding and inspired piece of work that they asked Lizette to add a historical introduction and submit it as part of her application for tenure. Lizette contented herself with the doctorate.

She had other plans.

That classical philologist never got his own doctorate. After Lizette had thrown him overboard, he took to drinking and behaving in a scandalous manner, and in the end they fired him as an incorrigible bourgeois. He now works in a bar in Ostrava.

While I was fulfilling my military obligations, Lizette's career progressed, though rather modestly at first. She got a job teaching Marxism at a Smíchov high school. Most of her fellow graduates had to become math teachers in the provinces, but Lizette made the timely acquaintance of someone influential in the Ministry of Education, whose name I forget.

By the time I got out of service, she had become program director in the Center for Folk Art. She'd appear in the Alfa Café bedecked with gold and precious stones, reminiscent of Geraldine's halcyon days, except that Lizette didn't have to reach into anyone's secret drawers. She had met someone high up in the Ministry of Finance, so that her family was well prepared for the fiscal reform.

As one might expect, Lizette's goings-on did not endear her to everyone, and there were growing numbers of fellows who hated her and voiced nasty insinuations about her whenever they could, but as soon as they found themselves vis-à-vis Lizette and vis-à-vis her bosom, they were bewitched once more into silent adoration.

Communists, noncommunists, Jews.

Fraternal equality.

Even Jan Vrchcoláb, the promising poet from the Youth Movement, fell for her. Lizette's bra blinded him to such an extent that he began to confide to her his ideological dreams and doubts. She told them to me. She had a liking for me, the snake in the grass, though she wasn't too generous with her sexual presents and though in the end she sent me packing, too.

Whenever Vrchcoláb was about to write something for *Youth Front* magazine, he first consulted Lizette. She gave him her advice. And because Lizette, like a true woman, shifted her moods and opinions with astonishing aplomb, Jan Vrchcoláb's opinions changed accordingly, often making a complete about-face. *Youth Front* readers ate it up. Thus, via Vrchcoláb, Lizette exerted a profound influence on the Youth Movement.

Of course, this was a secret.

Actually, no matter what ideas Lizette came up with, at bottom they all focused on one thing: Lizette herself. In that regard, she was remarkably consistent and loyal.

She kept changing Vrchcoláb's views just out of boredom, for the sake of fun. Many people started to scratch their heads, trying to puzzle out Vrchcoláb's philosophy. In vain.

Whenever she put some especially amusing notion into his head, we'd meet at the Alfa and enjoy the joke together. And we would collaborate on new nonsense to pump into him. He was in the habit of beating his gums in public about every new cultural or political event, and he was unaware that he'd become a dummy for a pair of ventriloquists.

His remarks, regularly reprinted in *Youth Front*, stimulated polemics and weighty discussions. Various socialist-realist theoreticians analyzed and expounded Lizette's bebop profundities, giving rise to a virtual new literary movement. Some articles were published in the Soviet Union, from there they were taken over by *L'Humanité*, then they appeared in *The Masses & Mainstream*. In this way, Lizette's influence extended across the Atlantic Ocean.

We developed an appetite for this kind of amusement, and began to target various prominent persons: via Vrchcoláb, we accused them of cosmopolitan, bourgeois nationalism, Zionism, Mendel-Morganism, formalism, and kowtowing to Western culture. We branded them as henchmen of Slánský or Tito, lackeys of naturalism, Freudianism, idealism, spiritualism, opportunism, revisionism, surrealism; we excoriated them for their fluency in English. Via Vrchcoláb, we carried on our campaign in private, at meetings, in the course of political evaluation sessions, and to some extent in the press.

Naturally, Vrchcoláb suffered the consequences. He is still suffering.

In the end, he managed to help place Lizette on the preparatory committee for the Sofia exposition, and thereby his usefulness for Lizette came to an involuntary yet definite end. Lizette's contribution to the preparatory committee proved predictably disastrous. But before she bowed out, she fulfilled one requirement set by the committee's director, Comrade Borecký: he asked the women employed by the organization to order, at state expense, three dresses from the fashionable Rosenbaum couturier, in order to represent our country abroad in a proper manner.

Lizette fulfilled this directive so ardently that she ordered not three, but six dresses from Rosenbaum's.

She screwed up whatever she touched, but the director became fond of her all the same. He called her "our Lizzy," even in front of the press. As a result, one young woman reporter, who had been ass-kissing Borecký in the hope that he would get her a job at the ministry, was encouraged to shoot an interview with Lizette for the upcoming exposition, presenting her as a typical socialist woman of our day.

Well, the reporter made quite a boo-boo, but nobody knew it at the time.

Before leaving for Sofia, there came a directive from above that the unduly overgrown staff was to be cut by a third. They threw out Maršíkova, who had been putting in two hours a day extra without pay. They threw out Béhmová, who had organized all the pavilions dealing with industrial machinery, light as well as heavy. They even threw out Tatyana Letnic-Sommernitz, who was political officer and supervisor of the Workers' Brigade.

History repeated itself once more: Lizette went to Sofia. She took along all six Rosenbaum creations, in addition to various items to trade and exchange. The cases of Riša's bass fiddle and my tenor sax were filled to overflowing.

You see, we went along, too. Zetka's Swing Orchestra. That was the only thing that Lizette managed to do right. When it came to gags and practical jokes, you could always count on Lizette.

And so we introduced Sofia to the folk music of the oppressed American blacks. We ourselves weren't oppressed in any way, although we were given strict instructions by the Ministry of Culture. We shot the works. Night after night, hundreds of male and female Sofians stomped and swayed on the floor, to the sounds of Benny Goodman. Lizette was among them, accompanied by various swains and later by a tall, blond man from their Ministry of Culture.

He, too, started calling her Lizette. Her name was actually Lidmila, but she had all sorts of nicknames: Lída, Liduše, Líza. That handsome Bulgarian called her Lizette, and it stuck.

After a few days they took off for a seaside resort. Of course, that was against regulations, the exposition was under strict discipline, but did that matter to Lizette? What a naive idea.

She joined us in Budapest, on our return trip, and she was escorted by a new admirer. He looked like an undercover policeman. The devil knows what he was, but with Lizette anything was possible.

She had brought back with her a TV set, a silver fox cape, a Persian rug, a calculator, two cameras, a gold watch and some twenty decagrams of gold jewelry. Also, six meters of Chinese silk with a pagoda design, but she sold it because Prague was overstocked with that particular item.

And she got away with it. The other women, each of whom was returning with one nylon nightshirt and two liters of maraschino, gnashed their teeth in fury. They hated her. Pokorná actually denounced her, but the report dissolved somewhere in the secret files of the Ministry of the Interior.

In Sofia, before she turned her back on the exposition and vamoosed with her blond companion, Lizette managed to bewitch the deputy director, Řeřicha, an extremely influential figure in education. He blazed up like an Olympic flame.

He arranged a public appearance for her. In the name of Czech women, she addressed the children of Bulgaria on the occasion of their new school year, and her speech was carried by all the Bulgarian media.

Back in Czechoslovakia, it was cited in the press.

She and I had composed the speech one early morning in the exposition dance hall, under the influence of heady Bulgarian wine.

Fortunately, nobody pays any attention to such addresses, and they are promptly forgotten.

Lizette, however, was not forgotten. Hardly had she returned to Prague and put in a voucher for an additional three thousand crowns in expenses than Deputy Director Řeřicha made her assistant editor of the State Pedagogic Publishing House. The candidate slated for that position, an experienced pedagogue, was suddenly discovered to be a dry intellectual of bourgeois origin, with insufficient Marxist erudition.

In comparison with Lizette's proletarian background, this was a serious shortcoming.

And because Lizette didn't have to start from the bottom, her deficiencies in elementary grammar never came to light.

You have to hand it to Lizette: she never forgot old friends. Trusted translators, employed for years by the publishing house, were dropped and translation assignments were distributed to Lizette's buddies instead. I benefited, too. With the help of a pocket dictionary, I translated from the Russian some poems of Mao Tse-tung, as well as a handbook of criminal law.

Lizette never learned of the disastrous consequences.

At a writers' congress, Lizette met a man from the Foreign Ministry. A month later she was named cultural attaché in Rio de Janeiro, in place of a fellow named Hrubeš who had been studying Portuguese for five years in expectation of the assignment.

I know, it sounds unbelievable, the mind rebels against it, and yet it's a fact.

There are many mysteries twixt heaven and earth.

Political evaluation, class origin, socialist zeal, merit, are one thing; generous bosom, shapely behind, green eyes are another.

Like time and eternity.

I don't know how you may feel about it, but I would never dare weigh one against the other.

Anyway, that snake in the grass Lizette who left so many in the lurch—including me—is in Rio, sitting pretty as cultural attaché.

I expect that one day she'll become the first woman president of this country.

And then at last we'll have real socialism.

krpata's blues

Got 'em blues, am' damn,
Mean to cry, O Lord!

THEY LOCKED UP KRPATA.
I wasn't surprised; in fact, I was glad. In my
opinion, it saved his life. For a while, at least.
During the four years that Krpata piped on the clarinet
with us, his performance of the blues improved remarkably.
When we took him on, Krpata had a decent technique, but
a hard, steely, even tone—no talent, it seemed, for making
the instrument sing—but he excelled at jokes and pranks:
for instance, maybe we're playing some big band Count
Basie, and I switch to tenor sax and sidle up to the microphone since it's my turn to show off with a solo, but when I
blow into the sax I get this horrible mooing sound. Of
course, the "sharp boys" in the front rows stiffen, the "sidecar girls" drop their preparations for an extra bumpy fox-
trot on the dance floor and stare at me in amazement, and I
blush and sweat and conjure up frightful noises—Zetka gets
up from the piano—I reach into the bell of the sax and pull
out a crumpled pair of pink nylon panties, monogrammed,

with lace. The gag sends the sharp boys over the edge, the bobby-soxers shriek enthusiastically, salvo after salvo of applause. I have to grin and bow.

That was the kind of prank Krpata used to pull.

Time-honored, but always effective.

And then he got married and the pranks started to dry up. And as they dried up, his clarinet began to weep and moan, his tone softened, it took shape, it got beautifully and lyrically rougher; during Dixieland jazz he would slowly steal the cornet's lead, until finally he took it so far that nobody danced during Dixie jazz; they listened close, shed tears, watched Krpata with his caved-in chest and tubercular face, with his half-closed eyes and that miraculous, sweet, bluesy woodwind, watched him play the blues.

What blues!

Really the blues.

Not infrequently, some sharp boy well on his way to getting drunk would burst into tears.

And now they've put him away for attempting to bribe administrators of the people's government and for libel of a police officer; they took away his clarinet and gave him a shovel.

That's how they saved his life, for a while anyway, because to keep playing the way he was playing was no longer an option. By now it would have gone beyond the limits of bearable. Best-case scenario, it would have driven him crazy, the way marijuana did to Leon Rappolo.

Krpata's story is as follows:

Out of love, he married a girl named Květuše Procházková, and out of light-headedness, he forgot to take care of the chief and fundamental thing, the most important thing in every love and every marriage: the apartment.

At this point, boredom is probably descending on you with the heavy pall of apartment anecdotes from the state humor magazine *Dikobraz*.

But this time it isn't an anecdote, but as it were, the true-life story of the private tragedy and artistic growth of Ladislav Krpata, blues clarinetist. Květuše was just a regular girl, a little peroxide, a little makeup, one day with her hair bobbed, the next day plastered down Roman style, another day plain Jane, long and straight—just like most girls, really, with the usual desires for a nylon nightgown and hand-knit shepherd's sweater from Italy for six hundred crowns.

He was the only one who could see what was special about her; I couldn't see it.

But that's the way it always is, isn't it.

Up until he hung her around his neck, he lodged in Žižkov with a lady named Rosalie Ledvinová, who rented the room exclusively to single gentlemen, because girls, she said, would always be cooking something and washing and drying, which makes a mess, and she didn't want any of that in the apartment.

With good reason. Aside from the three-by-four-meter room to let, she only had a kitchen, slightly smaller—unless you count the so-called antechamber. Relatively speaking, though, this widow was well-off, with a full four hundred in pension. Which, with the two-fifty she got from Krpata, came to a clean six hundred fifty.

Pretty good, hunh?

Of course, there are widows who do better, because they're resourceful widows. For instance, our drummer lives with one who instead of rooms has a boardinghouse. She has a kind of bungalow. It's listed as a family home; downstairs there's her apartment, on the second floor five cubicles, and in the attic another two. Seven altogether, with ten lodgers, all told. Three at two-fifty, in singles; eight at two-zero-zero (these are doubled up in cubicles); and one—how should I put it—one "honeymoon suite," the most expensive, actually: it costs fifty to a hundred crowns per visit. So that in total she gets twenty-one hundred a month out of the place, not counting the honeymoon suite.

You don't believe me? I can give you the address, if you're interested. There's no vacancy right now, although of course that one "suite" is always available.

But I've gotten sidetracked; this isn't what we're talking about here.

Krpata was living at the widow Ledvinová's at the time, and since he was naive and trusting, he followed her advice. Her advice was that he should never have anything to do with the housing department. For this reason, he lived in her house without a sublettor's license—that is, in his simplicity he didn't even know about the existence of this kind of document—he merely registered with the police and simply: lived there. The widow, just so you don't think ill of her, was not being crafty, not at all, but she was afraid of the housing department. Old women are always timid; they're afraid of vampires and murderers, and this one was afraid they would take her little apartment away from her and move her out to the border regions.

Well, now, the trouble was that Květuše Procházková was a proletarian daughter from Karlín and she lived with her parents in a kind of extra romantic apartment with a porch that faced a courtyard, like in Neruda's stories: you went from the porch into the main room, through the main room into the kitchen, and there the apartment ended. The apartment had another rare advantage: it was on the opposite end of the porch from the toilet, so you couldn't smell the septic tank, just laundry and rotten cabbage.

When the young couple committed their imprudence, they imagined that Květuše could move into Krpata's lodgings, and then when the widow Ledvinová kicked the bucket, they would grab the apartment.

Naturally, this was brutal and inhumane calculation on their part.

So in the end maybe they got what they deserved.

And Krpata should stew.

Only, it didn't work; they ran into the widow. She shrieked, the way widows shriek, that she had rented the apartment to a single gentleman, and if the single gentleman got married, he should look for an apartment elsewhere. She would not let another woman into her apartment; in her apartment, she said, one woman was enough.

To be honest, she was right.

Well, there was nothing to be done; they couldn't force the widow. For the first time, Krpata did a little research into the law on apartments; it astounded him that he hadn't read it sooner, but he figured out this much pretty quick: that a lodger has uncommonly few rights. Definitely not the right to move his wife in.

They decided therefore that while they were looking for an apartment they would live apart, she with her parents in Karlín and he at the widow Ledvinová's in Žižkov, which in the end wasn't so bad, because they weren't far from each other.

As for connubial bliss, they visited each other regularly. On Sunday afternoons Krpata went to Květuše's while her parents were at the soccer match, and on Wednesday afternoons Květuše came to Krpata's, because every Wednesday afternoon the widow Ledvinová went out for coffee. Of course, on Sunday they couldn't start before Květuše's parents went off to the soccer match, which took place at 2:30, and they had to be through by 6:30, when her parents returned from soccer, their mood altered according to the final score. On Wednesday it was even more meager, since they couldn't start until after 6:00, when Květuše flew in from the store, and they had to finish by 7:45, the latest Krpata could wait to go to work.

They filed an application for an apartment. They were placed in a category, assigned a number of points—I don't understand the system, because I don't care to; why should I care, when it doesn't have anything to do with me? I'm not longing for marriage and I have a place on Rajský Hill in a suburban home that belongs to a composer, with a view of Prague, a yard, a bathroom, and a telephone available for me to use. How did I get this, if I used to live like Krpata? Well now, that's a secret, sweethearts, and understandably so.

They gave Krpata points because he was married, because he lived in a sublet apart from his wife, because it was a house more than fifty years old, because there was no bath in his father-in-law's house, because the kitchen window faced north—but this was actually somewhat neutralized by the door to the main room, which faced south—because the apartment was damp, because it did not contain the required X square meters per person, because it had no gas, because it was a long way from the trolley car stop, because Květuše's father was an incurable bed wetter, etc., etc.

This, in short, was how they gave out points.

As time went by, the points started to increase. In the fall, water seeped into the apartment from the roof—there were quite a few points for that. Under the flooring in the kitchen they discovered mildew. More points. For the bedbugs in the main room, however, they refused to award any points, and merely recommended that they buy something to get rid of them, but on the other hand they did grant them something for the basement, which flooded when a spring of sulfur water suddenly gushed forth; later, however, the water turned out to be the fluid content of a burst sewage line, so they took the points back again. Krpata began to remind me of a stockbroker; he went to the housing department regularly, notebook in hand, adding up points.

He lacked one important thing. A child. They gave lots of points for that.

So they produced one.

And fortune smiled on them. When the child was born, the widow Ledvinová abruptly died.

She ate some spoiled salami that she had squirreled away ages ago and got meat poisoning.

But.

It was established that Krpata had no sublettor's license.

It was further established that he was married.

Consequently in the long run he had somewhere to live.

Consequently they flushed him out of the apartment, on the heels of the widow Ledvinová.

This, together with the child, drastically increased the number of points.

Well, except you would have to know Krpata, and his domestic jewel Květuše too. He's a dimwit. When they threw him out, he couldn't manage a word of protest. On the contrary. In his perverse, point-filled brain he saw it as a great blessing, and immediately and joyously rushed to the housing department so they could credit him with the points right away.

Well, why not? They credited him with the points.

And he moved into Květuše's parents' place. They weren't too happy about this. Hard to expect them to be happy about it, although as parents perhaps they were supposed to be.

But I have to describe this married couple a little. Květuše's mama was a Mother-In-Law with a big M, big I, and big L. She had a habit of standing with her hands on her hips; she had hips like that fertility goddess they unearthed in Věstonice and a facial expression like a French bulldog's. Need I say more.

She worked in the town market hall in Královské Vinohrady.

And Daddy paved streets for a living.

That's right. What d'you think, under socialism they no longer needed people to pave the streets?

Maybe now you'll understand that the day Krpata moved in with his wife's family, he vigorously stepped up his point-related efforts.

And his clarinet also began to acquire a cantilena tone and at the same time a rough timbre; it got more and more bluesy.

But somehow it seemed that they still didn't have enough of these points. They were already near the top of the chart, in maybe third or fourth place after a consumptive with two children and a fertile family without tuberculosis but with triplets and a second set on the way.

They couldn't budge from this position. Somehow, someone far behind them would always gain points suddenly and skip over not only them but also the family with potential sextuplets and the one with tuberculosis.

That "somehow" isn't as mysterious as it sounds.

But in this world you need a little smarts.

And that's what Krpata didn't have.

He played bluesier and bluesier blues, until finally, at long last, the light dawned and he realized he wasn't going to get very far with those points, and he would have to start cheating.

And once again he got lucky.

But once again he went about it in the wrong way.

He was all lit up with hope when he played *Tiger Rag* that night. He had the whole Bulvárka on its feet.

The plan involved a cousin who was supposed to be transferred from Prague to the border regions, where an apartment in a suburban home had been placed at his disposal. In Prague this cousin lived with his wife in a studio in a first-class modern apartment building with a lava facade in Pankrác, which must have seemed like paradise to Krpata.

This is what they dreamed up: they would take Krpata and Květuše on as lodgers, then they would move out, and

Krpata would take advantage of a certain paragraph and section of the law, according to which, if the owner of an apartment moves out, the sublettor has priority to it if he is married and has children.

With great ceremony, Krpata and Květuše and their son canceled their registration with the Karlín police and registered with the police in Pankrác.

They then went to request a sublettor's license. They were told there wouldn't be any problem.

The law, however, remembers everything.

They saw through the ruse, declared it to be an attempt at housing fraud, and told them to get lost.

For that matter, it's against the law for sublettors to move into a studio, especially it it's occupied by a husband and wife.

Still, they could be glad they didn't get in any serious trouble for it.

So they canceled their registration in Pankrác and reregistered in Karlín. And then nothing special happened to them.

Well, all right. Krpata went at the problem from another angle. He decided to build a do-it-yourself family home on Rajský Hill out of synthetic building materials. As a result he toiled through the whole prom season like a horse; he would make the rounds of maybe three proms a night; in the morning he helped out at the radio; in the afternoon he would play funerals with a brass brand; in the evening blues at the Bulvárka, and after midnight in some night club.

In a short time he had saved up the sum needed to purchase the synthetic building materials and the plot of land, and he requested a construction permit.

Again, of course, he did everything straightforward and aboveboard. It never occurred to him that even with synthetic building materials one should proceed somewhat differently.

He didn't look for protection, intervention, nothing.

He simply filed a request.

And on top of that he sent it by mail.

Simply put—Krpata.

As you can imagine, his application was processed smoothly. That is, negatively.

I thought he was going to have a stroke. He came to Barrandov one evening—it was already spring, the prom season was over, and we were playing outside on the terraces—his whole body was trembling and he looked like a nervous wreck. I took pity on him. He was already just a shadow of the old Krpata, of the one who stuffed ladies' nylon panties down the bell of my saxophone. I sat down next to him and got the whole story out of him. Afterward, when we played *Heartbreak Blues*, five trashed sharp boys and one quite sober lady burst into tears.

Then I took him in hand. Simply put—I'm not going to describe it to you in detail—look, here and there, we— pretty soon, things were progressing very nicely.

But during the waiting period, he and his wife came to visit me at Rajský Hill on a Monday night we had free.

We sat on the terrace; it was a warm evening, almost summer; against the light blue sky of Hradčany, the moon looked like a drop of honey someone was shining a flashlight behind; red light fell on the sunflowers on Petrin Hill; below us, the Vltava was full of dinghies and rowboats; trees rustled in the gardens along the hillside; reflections of green water in pools glanced through the fences of suburban homes—it was romantic, like a bad movie.

"Who lives here?" Krpata asked, his voice trembling with envy.

"You mean in this house?" I said. "Oh, some fellow named Bernát, a composer."

"Just him—in this whole house?" Krpata said.

"Yeah," I said. "I'm in this room, and the rest is his."

"And how many rooms does he have?"

"Three," I said. "He has a workroom, since as a composer he has a right to that by virtue of his occupation, then a bedroom, and then another room, since after all it's his house. And he's a composer."

"I don't know him," Krpata interrupted me.

"Your loss," I said. "It's not his fault you're just a jazz barbarian. He composes cantatas and songs for the workers' movement."

Krpata fell silent and surveyed the fantastic, formalist, purely cosmopolitan houses all around.

He gulped. Then in a loud voice he shouted: "Shit!"

Květuše rebuked him, primly.

"Calm down and breathe deeply," I said. "Don't yell at me here, or I'll have a real mess on my hands and that'll be it for your family home made out of synthetic building materials."

But Krpata again shouted: "Fuck me!" until it reverberated around the spire of the new boathouse down by the river.

"You moron," I said. "What are you yelping about? Be happy you're about to get a cozy home in the pipeline, a home made out of synthetic building materials and in the traditional architectural style of the Czech people, and don't trouble yourself with anything more than that, or you'll ef dot dot dot everything up again."

Even I didn't realize how timely my warning was.

But in the meantime there was a lesser mishap. I'd put the fix in with a certain gentleman regarding Krpata's synthetic home for five thousand crowns (the price of the gentleman, not the house), but the guy got thrown in the slammer. Several things blew up in his face; fortunately, ours wasn't one of them.

Krpata was back where he started, but five thousand lighter.

They nailed the gentleman right after the bribe.

When it rains, it pours.

So the little house made out of synthetic building materials melted away.

After this debacle, Krpata understandably began to have the impression that fate was at work here. He began to spend some time contemplating the bottom of his beer glass, which had one tragic consequence: Květuše suddenly found herself with another bun in the oven.

In Bulvárka, alcohol flow rose by twenty percent. In a sober state it wasn't possible to listen to Krpata play blues clarinet. It affected us too, made us let go, made us abandon ourselves to the music.

An American tourist offered us a gig at the Cotton Club. Dreamland.

And meanwhile Krpata, the idiot, without my knowledge, without telling anyone, started up on his own.

This time, as it later became clear, he was through with the straight and narrow, with application forms and the awarding of points; he was going to cheat.

Naively, the same way he'd grubbed for points and mailed in applications.

He drank like a fish, his cheeks darkened to an unhealthy shade of red, and his thin, bony fingers scattered over the clarinet like over calculator keys.

One night the cop sent to monitor Bulvárka to ensure no lewd dances were danced broke into sobs.

And then they nailed Krpata.

The idiot went to the housing authority right after some fuckup they had there, when they were all running scared and extra cautious, and he stuffed five thousand into the desk officer's pocket practically in broad daylight.

Naturally the guy exposed him on the spot.

He scored a few points as an incorruptible bureaucrat.

And they nailed Krpata.

When they took him away, he resisted arrest and made statements and even, they say, physically assaulted the police officer.

Now he's cooling his heels—actually, working like a dog—and as I say, maybe it's saved his life, for a little while.

Because the way he'd been playing the blues was the brink of suicide.

Naturally I don't know what will happen when they let him out.

But that's not my problem either, is it?

the bebop of
richard kambala

You probably don't know where Bop comes from—
Every time a cop hits a Negro with a billy club,
that old clubs says Bop! Bop!—Bebop!—Bop!

Langston Hughes

T HIS IS THE STORY of Richard Kambala, and may it remain his obituary. There won't be any words lost on him anyway, and they don't even put a notice in *Musical Review* when a jazz musician dies.

Especially when he kills himself.

Because it's like a confirmation of the formula that starts with cosmopolitan music, proceeds through hepcats, and winds up with existentialism and suicide.

For that matter, maybe the formula is true. I don't claim it isn't.

But why?

That *why* is at the beginning of all things, and at the end of them. And as for what's in between—

Well, some people know how to live even between those two *whys*, and don't give a damn if anyone answers them or not. But Kambala probably wasn't one of those people.

And so this is his obituary.

I don't know when he was born, but it was in Prague, and his father was in import–export. And it was definitely a wrong time to be born, for the son of a man who was in import–export.

That was also why they kept him out of high school. Naturally. Because what kind of fine feathered fellows would the cadre selection guys be, in the words of Charles Davida, if once in a while they didn't grab a millionaire's boy by the scruff of his neck when he was trying to squeeze through to a higher education, or if they didn't see to it now and then that some ex-prisoner couldn't get a job anywhere, except maybe as the most manual of laborers.

In this case, they were true to form and kept Kambala out, and instead they forced his best friend Josef Vořech to go—the perfect model of a country yokel who just happened to live in Prague, where his dad was overseer at the state farm in Jinonice. Josef Vořech! A red-headed kid whose ears stuck out like signal flags, who had loved cows and hay and the smell of alfalfa ever since he was little and who always wanted to go live in the country up near the border as soon as he finished grade ten. They forced him to go to high school, and he struggled to get through it like a camel through the eye of a needle, and then, when he wanted at least to go study agriculture—

Ah well, now he's still busting his buns at the College of Engineering, and Saturdays he sits at the Alfa Café, staring at us with watery eyes and crying. He's been crying ever since Kambala did it. He was his best friend.

Anyway, they forced Vořech in even though he had bad grades, because his father was a rural proletarian. They kept Kambala out because his grades were too good and he was the son of a capitalist and who knows, something might become of him and he might somehow harm the people's democratic regime.

So Vořech attended high school and Kambala was an apprentice at the Ringhoffer plant. Both of them were peeved.

Vořech floundered in high school like a fish out of water, occasionally boosted by some scared comrade professor, while Kambala did his best at the Ringhoffer plant. He crammed, he slaved, he was active in the Czechoslovak Union of Youth, he played guitar in the musical ensemble, he bellowed progressive songs and he wore a blue shirt to work.

He had no other choice, did he, wanting what he wanted. And finally he accomplished it. They accepted him at the vocational high school.

He was seventeen already. But they accepted him. He was recommended by his plant, so they accepted him.

When he made friends with us, he had been there a year. A strange case—he couldn't afford a trumpet, but he scrounged up an old fluegelhorn someplace, and that's what he played. We promoted him as a star attraction, hot fluegelhorn, world sensation, and he performed with us twice a week at the Boulevard Café.

Under a pseudonym, of course.

Meanwhile—and it was really touching—he still hung around with Vořech, the yokel from Jinonice. The cadre selection guys hadn't broken up their friendship. As a matter of fact, the two of them formed a fluegelhorn and vocal duo, which wailed and played at dances Sunday after Sunday in the villages around Prague.

I went to hear them once. You simply wouldn't believe that this could exist a few kilometers from the Boulevard Café and from Wenceslas Square. It was a tiny village in the Dobříš district, a tavern with a dingy dance hall, with a hand-lettered sign by the door which read: HOLIDAY DANCE, MUSIC BY MR. URAL'S BAND, 5 CROWNS A TICKET. And inside, the place was crowded with crackers like Vořech, girls with shoulders straight out of a fashion magazine imported from Moscow, smoke and liquor fumes, and on the old-fashioned platform with a carved railing sat Vořech and Kambala, each of them blowing his horn, accompanied by some old geezers on clarinet, fiddle, accordion, bass, and drums.

And every so often they would sing. God, it was enough to make you cry, even with all those stupidities, to see Kambala standing there, pale and dandy, with his hair in a d.a., and his aristocratic countenance, standing in front of the band with Vořech, arms around each other's shoulders, singing in that uniquely polka manner where nobody cares about details like having the same number of syllables as notes in their melodies. Singing, head to head, immobile except for their mouths opening and closing, Vořech's pancake ears glowing like a neon sign, sincere tears flowing from his blue eyes to his rosy cheeks. The two of them singing, Kambala carrying the melody in his tenor voice, deformed by the polka style, and above him Vořech, big and blustery—he could have swallowed Kambala after lunch—singing harmony in his eunuch's falsetto, slicing the syllables for all they're worth:

Where is that love
weshared . . . soften . . . derlee?

So while Kambala attended vocational high school, Vořech studied at high school until finally, with all the scared professors and informed commission chairmen, he was pushed through the sieve of matriculation exams. And then, by the same methods, they shoved him through the entrance exams at the College of Engineering, where he didn't want to go but where they were short of students. Now, if he was going to have to undergo all the unpleasantness connected with studying, Vořech would have preferred, as I have mentioned, to attend the College of Agriculture. But of course, in the end, he had to obey and go where society was supposed to have needed him most. Or so society thought. At least, that's what they said so they didn't have to say that they were simply ordering him to go there.

Naturally, Kambala had no trouble at all getting through vocational high school, it was child's play for him, and after school he studied college textbooks. Because that fool had set his mind on becoming a mechanical engineer.

Anyway—

Meanwhile, his dad, formerly in import-export, was working in a warehouse in Kbely. Then one day they arrested him.

We never did find out why. There was nothing about it in the newspapers, and Kambala didn't know for sure either. The only one who might have known was the dad himself, or maybe the prosecuting attorney knew—well, what can I tell you, you know how it goes.

That doesn't mean that I think he never did anything. I'm sure he did. Like maybe bad-mouthing current conditions, since he used to be in import-export. Or maybe telling a joke.

Or maybe he was in contact with enemy intelligence or maybe he was appropriating the property of the people.

I don't know.

Anything is possible.

Except that's not the point, where Kambala is concerned. The point was something else.

So Kambala played with us Wednesdays and Saturdays as Lajos Kerdely, Hungarian fluegelhorn player, a sensation in Budapest and the world. As sometimes happens—he was a relatively good-looking fellow—he fell into the trap set for him by Marcella Růžičková, whose name on posters was Cella Rose and who performed at various joints, singing songs like *Ghosts Riders in the Sky* and *C'est si bon* and various other hits of the early post-Stalinist era in Prague. In matters of the heart, Kambala was still a rookie, and so he glowed like the filament of a two-hundred-watt bulb.

The principal at the vocational school was a particular dope. For example, he had installed a huge alcohol thermometer with a sign: THERMOMETER OF LOVE FOR JOSEF VISSARIONOVICH STALIN. In the winter, they had to put an electric heater by it.

Enough said.

And then, in the autumn of the year of our Lord 1955, instructions arrived from the Ministry of Education, that in the interest of conscientious attention to the prudent selection of reliable cadres, children of citizens imprisoned for crimes against the state are to be dropped immediately from specialized schools, that is to say, kicked out.

It would be interesting to know what kind of thinking from what kind of brain gives rise to instructions like that. One is forced to recall, willy-nilly, the case of Dr. Bohadlo, that great progressive from Pankrác prison—but you know that story already.

Simply, the dope who was principal of the vocational high school obeyed, as is the wont of dopes, to the minute and to the letter. That is to say he went directly to the classroom of the fourth-year students, where they were just having a lesson in the Czech language, tossed Kambala out of the room bodily with his own two hands and a scowl of class hatred, and accompanied him outside in front of the school building, barely allowing him into the cloakroom to get his coat.

Later on, the Czech professor, a certain Milada Kalinová, a maid who could justly be called old, stood up for Kambala in the teachers' staff room, pointing out his excellent marks, his activity in the Youth Union, and finally something that she considered obvious, blind to the fact that it's not that simple: that children can't help the sins of their parents.

It slipped her mind that they often pay the penalty for them, however.

Well, old maids are frequently naive, there's nothing new about that.

Nor did she get away with it. The comrades in the staff room had for some time been observing her political instability, that is to say, comrade principal had been observing her, and the staff room went along with his observations. She received a strict reprimand.

Later on, I found out that for a similar affair—standing up for some student who had written some vulgar verse about the erstwhile Thermometer of Love—she had been fired.

Apparently, nobody missed her.

Actually, in those days the law about the exacerbation of the class struggle was still considered to be in effect.

But it did Kambala in.

First he fell apart, then he pulled himself together a little and began making a living with his fluegelhorn. Three evenings a week with us, Sundays and Saturday afternoons with Vořech and Mr. Ural's band, Thursdays at jam sessions at Drahňovský's nightclub with a bebop trio consisting of fluegelhorn, bassoon and drums, and the rest of the time, wherever. He made his way any way he could, and he clung to the aforementioned Marcella like flypaper.

He had an inner attachment to her.

Poor guy, he was simply young and inexperienced.

Because it's a commonly known fact that what appeals to women is a man, i.e., a Man, if not a MAN—but someone who hangs on to them, needs them, loves them to distraction, in fact so much that he can't live without them, someone like that merely annoys them.

In short, the same old story.

In Kambala's case it was just like that.

As long as he was Lajos Kerdely, sensation in Budapest and the world, a rather happy and frivolous kid with his hair in a d.a., who would occasionally go silly around Marcella when the situation warranted, but who for the most part let her run after him because his head was full of engineering and music and what they called the Future, Marcella could have doused herself with all the perfume in the world to at least get him to take a whiff of her. But when he melted like butter in someone's pocket, and began to look to her for understanding and something like moral support in life's difficulties, naturally, Cella was not amused, she was not impressed.

For that matter, what is there about that kind of behavior that could and would impress a woman?

Cella Marcella simply gave him the cold shoulder.

As for him, unfortunate fool that he was, after all the blows that his young life had dealt him he, naturally, went ahead and did exactly the wrong thing.

He wept, he begged, etcetera, he pursued her, he pled, sent her presents.

Marcella got together with Tony Bantam, a crooner from the Café Vltava.

One night in the men's room at the Café Vltava, Bantam took Kambala and turned him upside down with a professional clout, a left to the chin.

And then—

There isn't much more to tell. It was Thursday, and a bunch of us went to Drahňovský's club after work for a jam session. Around midnight, Kambala came limping in with his bebop trio. Without a word, they got up on stage, the fellow with the bassoon moistened his reeds, and then they let go and began to fall.

And fall they did—the way they fell, everyone there was sick to his stomach. And the people that go there for the most part aren't philosophers, but rather select hepcats and their very superficial lady friends. They fell in major seconds and in diminished fifths, down and down, immobile some-one put a blue spotlight on them and the people in the room quit talking, just gaped and listened.

And I'll never forget the way Kambala looked.

He stood tall and straight, his fluegelhorn twisted like a pretzel by his mouth, and as he toyed with the keys, you couldn't even see him inhale or anything. His face was expressionless. His eyes were on the edge of the bell or wherever. And he played—or God knows just what he was doing. Close by him the obscure little gnome of a guy with whiskers and a bassoon creaked and creaked and grumbled, while behind them De Martini scrunched down, softly rustling his cymbals.

Horrible music.

Existentialism in unwritten notes.

They played something, I couldn't tell what, nobody could tell, not even them, except probably Kambala, they played it for exactly thirty-seven minutes without a break.

Then they split.

The hepcats applauded for ten minutes more, but no-body came back, no encore.

Suddenly I was overcome with an evil premonition, I slipped outside, but Kambala was already gone.

I caught a streetcar and went after him. He lived in a villa in Strešovice, in an attic room that they rented out to him.

When I got there, it was raining. I climbed the fence and there was a light on in his room. Then I saw Kambala by the window in his pyjamas, brushing his teeth.

It seemed dumb to ring the bell and say something to him, besides, what could I say, in fact it began to seem to me that I had acted rashly and foolishly in coming. That I simply, well, have a strong reaction to music, and maybe this time Kambala had succeeded with his thirty-seven-minute uninterrupted bebop in getting Marcella and all the rest of it out of his system.

So I turned on my heel and went home.

Except it wasn't that way at all.

The next evening, Josef Voŕech burst into the Boulevard Café, his blue eyes reddened and tears streaming down his chin.

"Fellows, Kambala is dead," he says.

I jumped up, because it sliced through my spine like an electric shock.

"What?"

"Yes, guys," says Voŕech, pressing a blue farmer's handkerchief to his face. "He did himself in, guys, oh, oh!"

In short, it turned out that when Kambala finished brushing his teeth, he lay down on the bed, stuck a grenade in his mouth and pulled the pin.

If only yesterday I'd—

But what if I had. If they hadn't—

No, thinking about it in the conditional is useless.

And so this, then, is the obituary of Richard Kambala, hot fluegelhorn and bebop virtuoso, sensation in Budapest and the world. May at least his memory remain.

till death do us part

So I returned, and considered all the oppressions
that are done under the sun . . .

Ecclesiastes 4:1

WHEN YOU PLAY the tenor sax, sooner or later you ask yourself the question.

What's it really for and why and so forth and so on.

Life, that is.

The saxophone is, I'd say, the most revolutionary invention in the history of music. Because it speaks. Almost like a person; better, actually. It doesn't say words. It says essence.

Of course, Jack Teagarden, Kid Ory, etc. can speak on the trombone. And good old Dippermouth on the trumpet. And Billy Butterfield.

But the instrument that really speaks is the saxophone.

And the tenor sax, especially.

You can't sing on it like on the clarinet, or holler like on the trumpet, or roar like the trombone.

But you can speak.

It's the humanistest instrument in the world.

Just listen to it.

So a very good sax player sooner or later asks the question, especially because, when you earn your bread in some neon pisshole and instead of looking at the sheet music you look out at the waxed ring where both sexes twitch back and forth, you learn something about life.

Sometimes you learn quite a bit.

And then all of a sudden you're curious, what's it for and why and does it ever pay off.

Of course it's not a question they're handing out answers to.

You're only left with the dim suspicion that it's all the way it is just because—for its own sake, for fun, and for the sake of the joke—and that's no use to a person.

If at least a person knew for sure that one day he would wave his winglets and flutter through the cafés and see what the "sharp boys" and "sidecar girls" he used to know were doing, and how they were, before he ran out of gas.

I.e., died.

But the odds of that are negligible.

Better not to think about it.

And so one prefers to look around and observe people's fates.

Consequently, here they are.

For example, this tall, freckled, bearded man showing off with a gigolo's fox-trot à la 1929. And the black-haired, black-eyed girl with him.

Arnošt Karásek and Paulina Trnková, known as Polly.

She's not much good at polishing the dance floor, she sways back and forth in his arms somewhat as if she had a crick in her neck. He, as I said, is straight out of Café Lloyd, 1929. R.A. Dvorský and his Melody Boys.

When you consider what they've gone through.

Well, it's not anything sensational, I don't know what you're expecting. But in my opinion it's interesting and instructive enough.

Because it's so common.

Consequently it interests a person.

He's thirty-six, she's thirty.

It started when she was on vacation at her grandmother's in Červenky and nearly drowned. That was in 1940. She was fourteen. And he was twenty.

Of course, I didn't know them at the time. I know about this secondhand, partly from what Polly herself told me, partly from Lizette.

Lizette's apartment plays a role in this.

As does Lizette herself.

In 1940 Lizette was already a woman. With heels, breasts, lipstick, etc. She started early, with immediate success. They swarmed around her like the mindless bugs who fall for those ball-shaped, meat-eating plants in South America.

They marched right up, in double time.

And in line with all the others was Pollyanna. She loved her, as sometimes happens, so passionately that she wept away June nights. Letters, caresses, kisses, etc.—if she hadn't been fourteen years old, it would have fallen under the jurisdiction of the law against the third sex, which was still strictly enforced back then.

Lizette used her to run errands. Other than that, she didn't give a damn about her.

And while Pollyanna was carrying letters and notes and messages to Lizette's admirers and toadies, she naturally began to feel a little sorry that none of them were for her.

When she nearly drowned and Arnošt Karásek jumped into the Vltava in his Sunday pants, things came to a head.

The things that are always accompanied by mystery.

As in this case. Karásek fell for her, from his toes to the top of his ducktail *eman* haircut, which in those days was still called a *havel*. He fell for the fourteen-and-a-half-year-old, bony teenager with eyes like a frightened Indian monkey.

The same cannot be said of Pollyanna. But because he committed himself to her completely and because Lizette had a hoard of men and she had no one, she started to go out with him.

Go out, that is. At that age and in that era, it was not yet a synonym for sleeping together.

Naturally, a boy from Červenky, whether consciously and calculatingly, or unconsciously and instinctively, had goals in mind.

He set out to take her by storm.

But Pollyanna held the field. Lizette was there to offer wise and malicious advice.

She had this theory on the subject:

1: Kisses are the first step toward sex.
2: One should always finish what one begins.
3: A woman should be a princess, which means that
   she should only have one man in her lifetime.

Unfortunately I have to say that Lizette adhered to these principles only more or less. That is, insofar as they suited her.

But what the master does perfectly and with seeming thoroughness, the disciple-martyrs only bungle.

Pollyanna was soon mired in contradictions. She started kissing, but then she didn't want to finish what she'd begun.

She did seem like a princess, a real-life princess of course, not a fairy-tale one.

Lizette did not take into account that princehood is in reality more or less a governmental function and the prince's connection with the princess's sexual life is more or less symbolic.

But that would be getting ahead of my story.

Consequently Arnošt stormed and Pollyanna parried.

Out of despair he got involved in underground activities.

Arnošt, you should know, has freckles and a short temper. When something doesn't work out for him, he immediately gets drunk and plunges into despair. At that time, despair was a first for him.

He left for the Reich, where he became a spy.

At least that's what he said.

In any case after the revolution they gave him medals.

And that's when Pollyanna succumbed.

It happened in the Andre Hotel, Arnošt was in an Afrikakorps uniform with a Revo-Loot-ionary armband on his sleeve and he gave the maid a five-hundred-crown tip for the bloodstained sheet.

He was always big about these things.

But in this case things somehow didn't quite work out for him.

For this deflowering had strange consequences, as experiments like this sometimes have.

Arnošt went mad with passion.

Pollyanna lost all interest in him.

This is when the years of calvary began, a martyrdom that seems, when I glance out at the dance floor, to continue to this day.

It dragged out—or is dragging out—in periodic systoles and diastoles; see, Pollyanna alternately took him in and set him adrift.

As a rule, when she was attracted to someone with whom she hoped to experience Love, etc., it was Lent for Arnošt, and when she recognized she wasn't experiencing Love, he was allowed to come back again.

For there are two things here: Love, which has the habit of not existing, and Habit, which exists for goddamn sure.

Some people, mind you, have the good fortune, blessedness, ability, grace, lunacy, or whatever it is to experience Love. Usually they're nebbishes.

So maybe they just talk themselves into it.

By Love I mean Love that lasts a lifetime.

But by and large it always blows over in the long run. Later, sooner, too soon.

The first time she rejected Arnošt, he staged a scene worthy of the National Theater, so that Polly got scared and made the bed.

I met her just when the second period of rejection was reaching its climax.

At that time I had the opportunity—as did Pollyanna—to observe the auspicious blooming of Lizette's Love for

Robert, while I was left high and dry with respect to my affections for that princess. Observing this happy relationship also frayed Pollyanna's nerves not a little. Karásek went off on a slimming cure, and Polly started to search for a Love of her own with all her might.

Let me tell you, these kinds of attempts are hopeless. If you start to search, you've got it all wrong.

Because of course you can't search for these kinds of things.

Either they come or they don't.

The tragedy is, they usually don't.

That's the law of nature.

The messy part here was the fact that Pollyanna had her eye on me. As soon as she laid out the case with her big black eyes like a frightened monkey in the jungle, I said: Hey.

Hey, I said later.

Hey, Lizette said afterward. If you want to roll in the hay with Pollyanna, don't come crawling around my place.

Since a person is selfish where what he thinks is most important is concerned, within a single revolution of this earth on its axis, I didn't give a damn about Pollyanna.

I was sitting in Lizette's room the next day and I was talking to her like the Song of Songs, in order to appease her, when Pollyanna darted in, her eyes like an orangutan that had been frightened to death, and she handed us a letter.

She wasn't angry at me.

She was always really great that way.

In the letter Arnošt Karásek declared that he would wait until Friday for an answer in the affirmative. If he did not receive this answer by Friday evening at eight o'clock, he would lode his gun.

That's how he spelled it.

He wasn't entirely literate.

Pollyanna: What do I do now?

Look, didn't Arno say he was going to sell his Bugatti? Lizette asked.

That's what he said, Pollyanna replied.

Let's go, Lizette ordered.

Along the way she explained the plan.

I was supposed to pass myself off as a certain engineer Cincibus or something, interested in buying the Bugatti, who would go to Červenky to look at it on Saturday.

On Saturday, get it? When the question of whether Karásek lived till Saturday supposedly depended on Pollyanna.

I was for it; we called long-distance from the post office and in five minutes Arno was on the line. When I mentioned the Bugatti, it sparked his interest. He didn't talk like a suicide at all. He temptingly described the acceleration, how it handled, how much it guzzled per hundred kilometers. He told me in detail how to get to Červenky. Not until the end of the interview did something occur to him, maybe, because he pricked up his ears and wanted to know who had told me about this bargain.

I pretended there was something wrong with the phone line and cleared out of the phone booth.

I assured Pollyanna nothing would happen. Lizette made some cruel remarks and Polly calmed down.

And then Saturday morning a telegram arrived for Polly: Please come, I'm in the hospital. And—

—I have to say, he *was* in the hospital. When he didn't get an answer to his ultimatum, he shot himself. He said he aimed for his heart, but his hands were shaking so badly from excitement and rage that he shot into the muscle above the elbow.

Simply put, he hadn't hit his heart, but technically he had attempted suicide.

This was Polly's predicament.

What could she do: I wasn't working out for her as Love, so she went back to him.

Later she found out that he sold the Bugatti while he was still in the hospital.

At that time Arnošt was working as the director of all the coal-mining work teams in Ostrava district and he earned fifteen thousand a month. But he was no miser. It would be more accurate to say he had those fifteen thousand on the first of the month. In the evening he would get on the plane to Prague and the next day usually he didn't have them anymore. We all got hangovers from it. Me, Lizette, Robert, Zetka, the boys in the band, the brothers Mengele, everyone. And Polly the worst, of course.

Because she, poor thing, paid for his payday with her body.

And it dragged on like this for maybe another year. God knows if it had become habit, or if there was still compassion, or even in the end something like feeling.

Maybe the lack of any better opportunities.

This is at the bottom of almost all so-called great loves, and all of us, down to the last man and woman, make nothing but compromises.

From cradle to grave, as they say. It's not worth shit.

Excuse me.

Excuse me, ladies.

She went out with him in the figurative sense of the words and often we threw great parties. Maybe at the Mengele brothers' place, Theodore and Killian, madmen who avoided work and lived off the sale of pornographic photographs they manufactured themselves and even posed for, together with Killian's girl Vrát'a.

But what do you know, ladies. What do you know about the weight things have, the unbearable weight.

Not a damn.

But let me finish my story.

After a period of patience, it happened to Polly again. She longed for her so-called own life, i.e., for love.

We're all a little meshuggah now and then. From time to time everyone commits some sort of idiocy.

And she started up in two locations, with a Karel, who was a Communist, and with a Radoslav, who studied medicine.

Yeah, well—Polly was studying architecture.

At first Arno accomplished wonders. Drinking binges, scenes beneath her window, brawls, etc. Then he finally accepted it as the status quo and came to terms with his two colleagues.

They compromised a triumvirate.

What do you know about it.

But one day it blew up on Polly. Arnošt rushed into Lizette's place, his tie tangled around his back, his eyes like bloody moons, baring his teeth. Instinctively I sat down near the door, since I had Polly on my conscience, as you know, and with a temper like Arno's, you never know.

Disgusting, the pig, my God! Arno yelled, Italian-style. After a while it became clear that he'd subjected Polly to a physical inspection and discovered a disgusting thing. In the neck area she had seven blood-red contusions, technically known as hickeys.

Excuse my naturalism. I don't think another word for them exists.

Two had come from him. He remembered them. According to her own testimony, two were from Radoslav, one from Karel. Two and two plus one equals five.

But she had seven of them.

So who had she gotten the last two from?

She didn't know. She counted them wrong, that is, she had no idea how many she had, she got confused, and Arno had her cornered.

He insisted, begged, commanded, and finally whipped her with a belt. Then she confessed. A certain Jan Zábrana, 13 Birch Street, Prague, District XVI.

The impudence. On top of everything he lived on the same street where Arnošt's Prague apartment was.

And he was an architecture student.

A colleague, therefore.

Another time we were sitting at Lizette's, just her and me (Robert was out of town), right after an unsuccessful attempt at seduction on my part, a failure I was taking to heart.

I was feeling suicidal.

The doorbell rang.

Arnošt.

He staggered in, dressed in an Esterhazy suit and clutching a pigskin briefcase; the room immediately clouded up with alcohol fumes.

And he started roaring.

I.e., sobbing.

Lizette set about consoling him; suddenly Arno pulled himself together and again started roaring.

I.e., screaming.

That today he'll find out what's really going on, and if it turns out to be true, he'll shoot Polly and this guy, plus himself.

So what?

It appeared that he'd run into this architecture student and worked himself into a fury over his proprietary—or more precisely, shareholder's—rights to Pollyanna. And the guy took it calmly. Said it wasn't his doing, it was all Pollyanna. His role in the affair was entirely passive. All the activity issued from the girl's efforts. He would offer proof. That evening he was going to Pollyanna's for a tutoring session. It was a pretext devised for Pollyanna's parents, so he could come visit. He would leave the light on, and he wouldn't shut the window, which looked out on the garden. Arno could climb the pear tree in front of the window and decide for himself who was responsible.

At this point Arno stood up, shook off Lizette, pulled a filthy German automatic out of his briefcase, clicked the safety, and started waving it around, bawling.

Today he'd show them. All of them. All of them!

And he was looking at me.

I quickly forgot about suicide and slipped over to the couch, which was even closer to the door.

Then Arno pulled a Leica and a Swiss watch out of his briefcase. If anything should happen to him, these belonged to Lizette. For all she's done.

Then with a touch of pathos, he stepped out the door.

Lizette and I entertained ourselves with speculations about how it would turn out. We divvied up the things.

Lizette would keep the Leica, I'd get the Swiss watch. Outside it started to rain. For a while the heavens were absolutely prodigal with water.

The hours shuffled slowly by, until they stumbled up against two in the morning. Outside the window, the storm howled and howled.

At 2:05, Arno returned. No more Leica for Lizette.

No more Swiss watch for me.

Arno looked as if he were wearing a mud suit on top of his Esterhazy one. One of his cheeks was larger than usual, and in exchange, one of his eyes was smaller.

Yes. He'd climbed the pear tree and looked. He had a direct view of the divan. The guy came, stretched out, put his hands behind his head. Polly hopped on top, kissed him, caressed him, in short, behaved altogether immorally.

Arno shook with anger, and as he shook, so did the branch beneath him. He fell to the ground with a loud crash, and the guy poked his head out the well-lit window.

Well? Did you see? Am I right or what?

Arno pounced on him and dragged him out of the window down into the garden.

They exchanged a few blows, then Polly ran up and Arno gave her one across the face.

The architect burst out laughing.

He got one across the face from Pollyanna and he left.

Yeah, but otherwise everything was fine, Arnošt and Pollyanna said a few words.

Then they started up with each other again.

In a gold locket around his neck, Arnošt carried a curl that didn't come from Pollyanna's black head of hair, and he photographed the girl in her birthday suit with his Leica. He showed us the photos; Lizette borrowed them from him and passed them around to others.

Then Pollyanna received a letter. Concise. Polly, for God's sake, come!

Yours, A., c/o Ostrava County Prison.

He wasn't even able to write out his name.

Nonetheless Polly went, and came straight back. Arno was in the slammer for the rape of a minor. For the girl, the consequences were serious nervous shock and moderate bodily harm; for him the consequence was the loss of a tooth, which a cop knocked out for him when they deprived him of his freedom, which seemed too high a price to pay without putting up a fight.

They took the girl off to the asylum.

All this while under the influence.

With a forgetfulness usual in a woman, Pollyanna declared this meant the end between them. Arno could swear oaths regarding the strength of his love till Gabriel blew his trumpet, but she wasn't going to let herself be two-timed by him.

Karel, Radoslav, that architect, they didn't count. Me— I absolutely didn't count.

She got it from Lizette.

Once a guy starts going with another girl, man overboard! That was her slogan.

I happened to suit Pollyanna as well.

And that's how she left it with Arno.

But that's not how no prior record and valuable service to society, etc., left it. Within a fortnight he was out with a suspended sentence. Immediately he got drunk. He flew to Prague and staged a scene, but Polly didn't give in.

In despair he took up with a woman named Božena, an editor's wife. And bang, serious love. Arno was thrilled. Božena too, of course.

She left her husband and children at once, and set up house with her lover. She was a strong little lady and she talked as though none of it had anything to do with her. Arno dragged her over to Lizette's and when she explained how she had liquidated her marriage, it was like she was reporting on foreign affairs. At first her husband was angry, but since she remained calm, he calmed down too. Then he asked her, Boža, before you go, lie down on the couch again, undress a little, once more before you leave for good . . . You could hear the three dots when she told the story. And she lay down, after all that one thing had always clicked between them, she took off her dress and splashed on a little perfume. Her husband came back from the kitchen, he was carrying something behind his back, and when he got up close to her, he pulled it out and it was a whip and he thrashed her naked backside.

That's what she told us.

All the while, she was eating Lizette's little open-faced sandwiches one after the other.

They divided up their possessions. She discovered that he had cut delicate incisions in both her skis with a hacksaw, so she would fall flat on her face when she went skiing that winter.

Arno was sitting beside her. From time to time he would stroke Božena's spherical attractions, somewhat lost in thought.

When she moved her wardrobe into Arno's efficiency at 16 Birch Street, they demolished the banisters.

I tried to picture Arno's studio, Božena's wardrobe, and Božena, all three together, and it didn't fit.

It was too much.

Arno got a little buzz on.

By the following Saturday he had caught gonorrhea in Ostrava and Saturday night he infected Božena.

But Bernard supplied them with penicillin, so they didn't get registered at the VD office. Yeah, Christ, Bernard the kleptomaniac, the one who got together with Iwain to part Geraldine from those two thousand crowns. Same guy. They employed him at the penicillin factory. And today— he's a student. The factory okayed him to go off and study biochemistry.

A doctor helped them out with penicillin for a largish smallish bribe.

Of course the serious love affair cracked up over this.

Or whatever it was.

Božena flew off to visit her aunt in Bratislava. By chance the editor was loitering there as well. They rode back together in the same sleeping car. They sent movers to pick up the wardrobe.

Arno got the bill for the movers.

He paid it.

He was big about it.

And Polly took him back out of the goodness of her heart.

So, ladies, do you get it yet?

More of Polly's loves ensued. I don't know which came first, Rais the psychiatrist or Fikola the army welterweight champion.

Then Arno married Ellinka and quickly divorced her.

Then Polly married a dentist named Sudrab and cheated on him for a year with Arno.

Then he divorced her.

Then—I don't know any more. It's a story that's always the same and probably will be. Arno came back to her bed like malaria, and maybe it is some kind of chronic disease. Maybe black-haired Pollyanna suffers from European malaria like everyone else who tries and searches and would like to give herself, but doesn't have anyone to give herself to.

Like everyone who's doomed that way. Who would have been better off if as spermatozoids they had thought twice before battling their way through the egg cell's rind.

But given the life span these spermatozoids have. Unpleasant. Senseless.

In the end they break into the cells, and this is what you get.

Pollyanna, for example.

And so they march to the rhythm of the boogie-woogie, I philosophically play out for them my eight eighth notes

per measure, and Marcela Růžičková sings a running commentary with the words of a classic blues song, which she's
adapted to the female gender:

I can't use no man
If he can't help me lose the blues . . .

Maybe it'll go on like this for another twenty or thirty
years.

There's nothing that would save them from it.

There's no saving some people.

Some people are put here only to join society's efforts
and through their labor to build the world that other people
live in.

But they live.

Not like Polly and the rest of them here.

dialogus de veritate

Pilate saith unto him: What is truth?

St. John, 19:38

T HAT FELLOW reminded me of someone the moment he arrived. He came in about nine, and sat down at a table right under the stage. He looked exactly like somebody I knew, but who?

He ordered a carafe of wine and stared at me. After a while it got on my nerves. One glass after another, and the guy stares and sips and gapes. Damn!

Sure, there are hepcats who gawk. They gawk at your fingers, at your sax, at your face. But you can tell they're music fans. This guy was staring at me, not at the way I made music.

During break, as I got up to go to the toilet, I saw the guy getting up, too. And sure enough, as soon as I found myself among the tiles and started to relieve myself, he was right beside me, legs spread wide, staring up at me!

That really made me mad.

Look here, mister, I started, but he just lowered his eyelids and said: Hi, Smiřický.

And then I recognized him.

Dunca Brom.

I almost pissed on my pants, I was so startled.

Pardon me, ladies. Pardon me.

Dunca savored my embarrassment, and then said:

Sure, it's me, personally, minus mustache. And my hair got darker.

I swear to God. Dunca used to be blond, and now he was as black as an eclipsed sun.

And the Gable mustache was gone.

I looked around. The sign on one of the toilet doors read: OCCUPIED. I put my finger on my lips, and Dunca smirked.

Great. Is that something new around here? A kind of secret Masonic sign?

That's right, I said. Let's go. We sat down at his table. I glanced at the stage. Nobody was there yet, and people were still chatting in the hall. I turned to Dunca.

This really is a surprise . . .

I need a place to stay, he said matter-of-factly.

That put me in a painful situation. I would have enjoyed shooting the bull with him, that wasn't it—the problem was simply . . . Well, I've always been a champion of caution, staying out of trouble, neutrality. That was my kind of wisdom. And it always paid off for me. And now, suddenly . . .

Natch, I said. Or rather, my mouth said it. Naturally. After all, I couldn't bear to lose face. Not after that unquestioning confidence he had shown me.

Where do you live? Still on Rajský Hill?

Right. Everything's still the same.

Dunca raised his eyebrows. Sure, it was him. That slightly

too handsome, movie-star kisser under that new shock of black hair.

Everything?

Natch, I said. That's obvious, isn't it?

Great, he answered. I see that I knocked on the right door.

Unfortunately, I thought to myself. But aloud, I said: So what's been happening? Tell me.

Let's wait till we get home, OK? Hey, look at that pretty chick over there, he said, and winked at a sultry brunette à la Dolores del Río. But I think her name was Havašíková, or something like that.

The brunette responded with a vague smile.

Knockout knockers, said Dunca.

Sure, it was him all right.

Zetka and Davida climbed up on the stage.

I've got to go now, I said. Shall I wait for you afterward?

Don't worry, he said, and got up. I got up on stage and we started with *Bigwig in the Wigwam*. I watched him and saw him spinning Del Río–Havašíková around her own axis on the dance floor.

I didn't feel good about the whole thing. I know from experience—other people's, not my own—that once you stick your foot in the water, you'll end up dripping wet sooner or later.

But there are certain situations . . . All I had to do was to go to the phone, dial—and I'd be in the clear. In fact, I'd greatly improve my political rating.

Needless to say, nothing like that entered my mind. I am a coward, a parasite, a hipster, I am lazy and often use vulgar expressions in mixed company. I have plenty of other faults as well.

But I am not a scoundrel.

And so at midnight, after the last number, I wiped the sax dry, picked up my windbreaker and headed for Dejvice. A trolleybus took me up Rajský Hill. Dunca was nowhere to be seen. Only after I unlocked the garden gate did he emerge out of the shadows. That's the first sight I had of him since watching him twirl Havašíková on the dance floor.

Man, he had really learned how to keep a low profile.

I closed the gate, we quickly walked up the path to the house and upstairs to my room. As soon as I turned on the light Dunca plunged into an armchair.

Don't worry, he said as if he read my mind. My buddy with whom I was supposed to stay tonight is arriving tomorrow. I'll be gone by morning.

No problem, I said. I was as full of sudden happiness as an amnestied prisoner.

In my joy, I just couldn't do enough for him. Would you like some coffee? Or a drink?

What have you got? he asked mistrustfully. I opened the liquor cabinet, where I had half a bottle of Key Island rum and some Pont Neuf brandy from Hungary. Dunca took one look, and said: Just give me some coffee.

While I was making coffee we kept silent. I brought two cups to the table and sat down facing Dunca.

Here we are, he said.

Man, I said, how in hell did you get involved in that stuff?

He shrugged: A man should change his occupation once

in a while, otherwise he grows stale. I discovered I had an unsuspected talent.

It would seem that way, I said.

He threw me a dirty look.

Why don't you try it too, chum?

No way. That's not my cup of tea.

You know English, he said, ignoring my last remark. You've got a nose for opportunities. He glanced around. I'd guess that this cozy little flat is the fruit of considerable diplomatic talent. In fact, given the present circumstances, one might say an unhindered talent.

Sure, but . . .

Here you're just shit, and you'll stay shit. As long as those jerks stay in power, you'll stay shit. You know that, don't you?

Sure, but . . .

And you don't want to give up jazz, he said.

Look here, Dunca, I said. Let's get things clear. I'm shit, and I'll stay shit as long as those jerks are around. But it's better to be shit than a number in a striped shirt, don't you agree?

Good Lord. You talk like Dolores Ibarruri La Passionaria, only ass-backwards.

And so I prefer sitting here on Rajský Hill than somewhere else. Like a refugee camp in Krautland.

He seemed to turn sad. But he was probably just play-acting.

Et tu, mi fili, he said mournfully. You starting to believe those jerks?

Nonsense, I answered. But quite a few decided to come back, didn't they.

Listen to me, Dunca said. You'd have no need or desire
to come back. Fools, cowards and total zeroes come back.
But not anybody with an ounce of brains in his skull. Except
the way I came back.

OK, I said.

Seriously. We'll make a deal and I'll get you out.

No thanks.

There'll be absolutely no risk as far as you're concerned,
Dunca said. I'm doing it strictly out of friendship. I'll just
take care of a little business here and then you'll get a free
ride. I have a guaranteed leak, don't you worry.

I see, I said, and started to perspire.

Believe me, a piece of cake. No crawling on our bellies,
no cutting of barbed wire. A big shot in the border guards is
in with us. It'll be like a stroll along the Moldau.

Listen, Dunca. I believe everything you say and I'm
grateful to you for thinking of me, but no. Thanks a lot, really, but no.

He probed deep in my eyes.

So you really don't want to?

No.

You're scared, aren't you!

No, I answered, although I was. But actually it wasn't so
much a matter of fear. At least, it wasn't the fear of frontier
guards or anything like that. It was something else.

You're lying, Dunca said. You're a shitass, like you always were.

Have it your way, I said. If that's what you think . . .

I have friends in Radio Free Europe. You're a born story-
teller. You could sell them stuff for good money. You know

lots of stories, you were always good at making up stories. And there's your sax . . .

No, Dunca, forgive me, but it's no deal.

But why, for heaven's sake? Do you ever think about what goes on around you?

This might surprise you, but I think about it all the time. Maybe you think it's crazy, Dunca, but I'm a socialist.

Listen, man, I'll believe everything else, but not that.

You don't have to.

But even if you were, which I don't believe for a minute—what does that have to do with this country? Is this your idea of socialism?

Something along those lines, I said.

Dunca stared at me, wide-eyed. Along what lines? We had a similar bunch here not long ago, if you remember, along national socialist lines. They didn't care much for jazz, either.

Listen, I said. I may not be crazy about the Party or about the government. I'm only trying to be objective.

Just like the people's supreme tribunal, said Dunca.

First of all: if I came with you, I'd probably starve.

I told you I have friends in Radio FE.

Maybe you do, but I'd never work for them. I'm not a political animal. Politics demands that you get all worked up and bullshit about ideals. That's not my style.

But you say you're a socialist, Dunca objected.

I know it sounds funny, but yes, something along those lines.

Along their lines? All those stupidities of theirs you see all around you, they don't bother you?

They bother me.

And what about all the rest of their swill?

Listen, I said. I know about the swill better than you do.
I see jerks and idiots in high places who know as much
about governing as a pig knows about pianos. And they play
with people's lives like it was all a big game.

And yet you're something like a socialist, said Dunca.

Because this regime has little to do with socialism.

There I agree with you, Dunca said. Except maybe of
the national kind.

Nobody is going hungry, I said.

You don't seem to be well-informed, said Dunca. Just
ask a retired fellow trying to manage on a two-hundred-
crown pension. I guess that such people must atone for the
good jobs they had before the war.

Even if that's true, you're talking about a small minority.
The vast majority have plenty to eat. I sensed that I was just
beating my gums, and felt like an awkward fool.

You're going to make me puke, said Dunca. You babble
about hunger like a political instructor after a week's schooling. Have you ever gone hungry?

No. And neither has anybody else.

Christ Almighty, said Dunca. And it doesn't bother you
that you've got to turn yourself into a whore? Think one
way and talk another, suck up to people you'd rather kick in
the ass? Keep turning around to see who's behind you, keep
your finger on your lips like it was glued there?

I don't like these things any more than you do. But if
you insist on talking about it . . . Sweat poured down my
back. I'm bullshitting, I thought to myself, I've blown it. I

said: It's all a matter of a scale of values. I believe—not because I like it, but because it's probably the truth—that the
highest value, to put it crudely, is a full stomach. Because
that's a law of nature. And also the certainty that I'll always
have the possibility of making a living. And when I won't be
able to work any longer, the state will take care of me.

You seem to think of socialism as a system for producing
pensioners.

Something like that, I said.

And you believe that? Dunca said, gaping straight at me.

No. I don't know. I only believe: some day. I simply believe in decently dressed people, guys on motorcycles and
girls in nylon blouses.

A new stage of Marxism, Dunca grumbled. Nylon socialism. The way it looks to me, your ideas of the West
come out of *Progressive Perspectives*. Torn pants and starved,
sunken faces.

Maybe not now, I said, and my shirt felt like it was pasted
to my back. But once a depression hits . . .

Straight out of *Progressive Perspectives*, Dunca broke in.
Listen: I bet they taught you that during the Depression,
America had twelve million unemployed, while the USSR
didn't have a single one.

Well, isn't it the truth? I said, and glanced at my feet to
make sure sweat wasn't dripping out of my trouser legs.

It is, Dunca nodded. But what they didn't tell you is how
many people they had stashed away in Siberian concentration camps.

Maybe you're right. I never thought of that. I shifted in
my chair. My pants, too, were beginning to stick to my body.

So it's just about fifty-fifty, said Dunca. You can choose between northern lights and unemployment insurance.

I fell silent.

And all this nonsense they've got here, Dunca said. Do you think it's necessary? Do you think there's no other way to introduce socialism?

I don't know, I said. They introduced it here.

Yeah. But seriously: do you really put the full stomach of some beer-guzzling lout higher than culture? Higher than that jazz of yours, higher than a life worthy of human beings?

I turned stubborn.

First you've got to have a full stomach before you can . . .

Dunca shook his head. *Progressive Perspectives.* All right, I give up.

I shrugged.

Duncan suddenly flared up: You really believe, he said, his voice quivering with excitement—that if these bastards ever succeed in gobbling up the world—you think that under their wise leadership the world will be worth a shit, you think life will be worth a damn?

I don't necessarily believe that, I said, beginning to feel feverish. I simply don't know. Probably—yes.

Can't you see, since you claim you know them so well, that all they'll ever accomplish is to eliminate hunger, maybe, and maybe they'll even play Beethoven, but you can bet they won't produce any new Beethovens. And if by some error of planning one were to appear, they'd make sure he wrote odes to the Party rather than odes to joy. Is this bunch of bastards going to save the world? At best they'll turn the world into a well-fed prison. But of course, for you a full stomach is the highest possible value.

For the time being, I guess it is. Of course, if things ever turn out the way you described, then it's a different matter.

If, according to you, a full stomach is the highest value of life, Dunca said, speaking very slowly, then be good enough to tell me: how is a human life different from that of a cow or a pig?

The conversation was really upsetting me. I was soaking down to my shoes. What the hell was the point of all this, what did I know about politics, anyway? I'd much rather have played my sax for him, but it was getting close to dawn.

For the present, there is probably very little difference.

That silenced Dunca.

We gabbed a bit more, but in the end Dunca got disgusted, lay down and fell asleep, and I went to the bathroom to hang things up to dry.

I admired his nerves. If I were in his situation, I wouldn't be able to sleep a wink.

In the morning, he said good-bye.

You change your mind about coming? he asked.

No, Dunca. Forgive me.

Well, OK then. Ahoy, and thanks!

Thanks, and lots of luck, I said.

Then he disappeared.

This was two months ago, and I haven't seen him or heard about him since. I kept reading *Progressive Perspectives*, but there was no mention of any arrest.

So that's the story. I play the sax, and continue living here. I don't want to get involved. Maybe it isn't just a matter of fear. I don't know. All I know is that I don't want to get involved.

Maybe you think I'm a jerk. But everything I told you, about getting nabbed, about Geraldine, Kambala, Lizette and all the rest, that's the God's own truth.

Then again, what do I know about the truth, or about the way things are going to turn out. Pilate, that's me.

As for myself . . .

But I've gabbed long enough.

And forgive me, ladies, for the vulgarities that crept in here and there. I'm really sorry about that. If I'm ever able to get this published, I'll drop all the dirty words and put in decent expressions. You'll pick them out yourselves.

You see how I respect and honor you.

So maybe I'm not such a bad fellow after all.

With your permission, I take my leave.

Sweet dreams.

Good night.

Written 1954–1956 in Prague